Irish Family History on the

A Directory

D1644750

THIRD EDITION

Stuart A. Raymond

THE FAMILY HISTORY PARTNERSHIP

Published by
The Family History Partnership
PO Box 502
Bury, Lancashire BL8 9EP

Email: sales@thefamilyhistorypartnership.com
Webpage: www.thefamilyhistorypartnership.com

in association with
S.A. & M.J. Raymond
P.O.Box 35, Exeter EX1 3YZ

Email: samjraymond@btopenworld.com
Webpage: www.stuartraymond.co.uk

ISBNs:
The Family History Partnership: 978-1-906280-01-7
S.A. & M.J. Raymond: 978-1-899668-38-0

First published 2001
Second edition 2004
(published by FFHS (Publications) Ltd.)

Third edition 2007

Printed and bound in Europe at the Alden Press, Oxfordshire

Contents

Introduction

A vast amount of information concerning genealogy and family history is now available on the internet. Surfing the net can be a very productive process for the researcher; it can, however, also be very frustrating. There are thousands of genealogical web sites worth visiting, but the means for finding particular irrelevant sites are very poor. Search engines frequently list dozens of irrelevant sites, but not the ones required. 'Gateway' sites are not always easy to use. Links are not always kept up to date. It is easy for relevant sites to escape attention.

I hope that this directory will enable you to overcome these problems. It is intended to help you identify those sites most relevant to your research. The listing is, inevitably, selective. I have only included those sites likely to provide you with useful information. Sites devoted to particular families are excluded: a listing would occupy at least a whole volume. I have also excluded passenger list sites dealing with single voyages: again, a full listing would be extensive. Sites of general interest, e.g. search engines, maps, *etc.,* are also excluded. Many of the sites I have listed, and especially those in chapters 1, 7 and 8, can be used to find sites excluded from this directory.

A detailed discussion of family history sources on the internet is provided by RAYMOND, STUART A. *Netting your ancestors: tracing family history on the internet.* The Family History Partnership, 2007.

This listing is as up-to-date as I have been able to make it. However, new web pages are being mounted every day, and URLs change frequently. Consequently, it is anticipated that this directory will need frequent updating. If you are unable to find a site listed here, then you should check Cyndis List or one of the other gateways listed in chapter 1; the probability is that the site has moved to another address. Alternatively, search words from the title - or the URL - on a search engine such as **www.google.com.** It is frequently the case that sites which have not been found directly can be found in this way.

If you know of sites which have not been listed here, or which are new, please let me know, so that they may be included in the next edition of this directory. Over 700 web pages are new to this edition; in particular, there are again much more extensive listings of sites relating to births, marriages and deaths, and to monumental inscriptions.

My thanks go to Cynthia Hanson, who typed this book, and to Bob Boyd, who has seen it through the press.

Stuart A. Raymond

1. Gateways, Search Engines etc.

There are a variety of gateways and search engines for Irish genealogists. One of the most useful is Genuki, which itself provides a great deal of general information. Cyndis list is the major international gateway; it has an American bias, but nevertheless provides numerous links to Irish sites. Quite a number of sites offer similar help, although the 'international' ones tend to be biased towards U.S. genealogy. General search engines are not listed here; they may be found on Cyndis List, or by accessing some of the other sites listed below.

- Genuki Ireland
  www.genuki.org.uk/big/irl

- Cyndis List of Genealogy Sites on the Internet: Ireland & Northern Ireland
  www.cyndislist.com/ireland.htm
  The most extensive listing of genealogical websites on the internet, which has also been published in book format:
  HOWELLS, CYNDI. *Cyndis's list: a comprehensive list of 70,000 genealogy sites on the Internet.* 2nd ed. 2 vols. Baltimore: Genealogical Publishing, 2001. Now (mid-2007) 264,800 links and expanding rapidly.

- Roots Web Genealogical Data Cooperative
  www.rootsweb.com
  Home to thousands of genealogical mailing lists, the Genweb project, web sites, *etc., etc.* American bias, but also of Irish interest.

- Ireland Genealogical Projects: The Original Ireland Gen Web Project
  irelandgenealogyprojects.rootsweb.com
  Lists county pages, query pages, *etc.*

See also:
- The Ireland Gen Web Project
  www.irelandgenweb.com/

There are a variety of other gateway sites:
- All English Records.com: Ireland Genealogy Records
  www.allenglishrecords.com/ireland
  Gateway

- The Celtic Connection
  www.geocities.com/Heartland/Prairie/8088/ire.html
  Gateway mainly to county websites

- Genealogy Ireland Eire History
  www.members.tripod.com/~Caryl__Williams/Eire-7.html

- Genealogy Resources on the Internet: Irish Genealogy
  www-personal.umich.edu/~cgaunt/irish.html
  Gateway

- General Ireland Genealogy Links and Resources, & Genealogy Chat Room
  www.looking4kin.com/genire.htm
  Gateway

- Ireland Genealogy Links
  www.genealogylinks.net/uk/ireland/
  Gateway

- Ireland Genealogy: UKI search.com
  www.ukisearch.com/ireland.html
  Links page

- Ireland: Web Sites for Genealogists
  www.coraweb.com.au/ireland.htm
  Links page

- Irish Genealogy Pages: Genealogy Online Resources for Ireland
  www.scotlandsclans.com/ireland.htm

- Irish Ancestral Pages
  www.geocities.com/irishancestralpages
  Includes various small databases

- Irish Family History: specific Irish Genealogy Sites
  www.nzsghamilton.co.nz/ireland.htm
  Gateway

- Irish Genealogy
  www.daddezio.com/irshgen.html
  Gateway

- Irish Genealogy Links
  www.geocities.com/SiliconValley/Haven/1538/irish.html

- Irish Genealogy on the Net
  irishgenealogy.net/
  Gateway

- Irish Heritage & Genealogy Links
  indigo.ie/~rfinder/Links.html
  Gateway

- Irish Resources on the Internet
  www.genealogy.com/30__links.html

- Searcher: the Irish Genealogy Search Engine & Directory
  www.ireland-information.com/irishgenealogy

- UK Genealogy.Ireland Research
  www.ukgenealogy.co.uk/ireland.htm
  Covers Eire and Northern Ireland

- What's What in Irish Genealogy
  indigo.ie/~gorry
  Gateway to quality sites

Many Irish genealogical sites may be found by commencing at one of:
- Discover Ireland Genealogy Web Ring
  www.accessgenealogy.com/rings/ire

- Discover Northern Ireland Genealogy Webring
  www.accessgenealogy.com/rings/nire

For a gateway to Irish genealogy in Canada, visit:
- Irish Genealogy in Canada
  layden-zella.tripod.com/IrishGen.index.html

If you want to place your research in the wider context of Irish history, see:
- Irish History on the Web
  larkspirit.com/history/

Sites which are no longer current may still be read at:
- Internet Archive Wayback Machine
  web.archive.org/web/web.php

2. General Introduction to Genealogy

Numerous general guides to Irish genealogy are available on the internet; most provide similar basic guidance. Many family history society sites (chapter 4 below) have beginners' guides; so do many of the county pages listed in chapter 7. Some of the pages listed below are extensive - especially those from major institutions.

- Centre for Irish Genealogical and Historical Studies
  homepage.tinet.ie/~seanjmurphy
  Includes 'Directory of Irish genealogy', *etc.*

- Directory of Irish Genealogy
  homepage.eircom.net/~seanjmurphy/dir/

- Family Search Ireland Research Guidance
  www.familysearch.org/Eng/Search/RG/frameset__rg.asp
  Guide from the Latter-Day Saints - scroll down to 'Ireland'

- Fianna Guide to Irish Genealogy
  www.rootsweb.com/~fianna
  Extensive, including county pages, and many databases

- Finding Your Ancestors in Ireland
  www.genealogy.com/genealogy/4__pocket.html?Welcome=1083401080
  For the descendants of emigrants; includes brief notes on sources in Australia, Canada, New Zealand, the U.S.A. and the U.K.

- From Ireland
  www.from-ireland.net
  Extensive

- Genealogy: Where and How do I Research in Ireland?
  www.12travel.com/ie/information/genealogy.html

- How to start your Irish Research
  www.genealogy.ie/gettingStarted.html

- How to Trace Your Family Tree
  www.proni.gov.uk/research/family/family01.htm

- Ireland Research Outline
  www.familysearch.org
  Click 'Search', select 'Research Helps', choose places beginning with I, and click title.

- Irish
  www.genealogy.com/00000374.html
  Brief introduction

- Irish Abroad: Irish Genealogy Expert
  www.irishabroad.com/YourRoots

- Irish Ancestors
  scripts.ireland.com/ancestor
  www.ireland.com/ancestor
  One of the best sites: hundreds of pages

- Irish and Irish-American Family Research
  mypage.siu.edu/edoday
  For American researchers

- Irish Ancestors.net / Sean E. Quinn
  freepages.genealogy.rootsweb.com/~irishancestors

- Go Ireland.com: Genealogy
  www.goireland.com/Genealogy

- Irish Genealogy and History Articles
  globalgenealogy.com/globalgazette/irish.htm
  Collection of articles, some listed here separately.

- Irish Research /Lyman D. Platt
  www.genealogy.com/4__irsrcs.html
  Brief introduction

- Irish Research: Suggestions for the Beginner / Kyle Betit
  globalgenealogy.com/globalgazette/gazkb/gazkb33.htm

- When Your Irish Parish Registers Start Too Late
  globalgenealogy.com/globalgazette/gazkb/gazkb35.htm

- What's What in Irish Genealogy Directory Page
  indigo.ie/~gorry/Dir.html
  Basic information, including details of societies, record repositories, events, *etc.*

- Your Irish Roots
  www.youririshroots.com
  Introductory pages
- Seventeenth Century Sources
  freepages.genealogy.rootsweb.com/~irishancestors/Add17.html
  Introduction to *Inquisitions Post Mortem*, Patent Rolls, various muster rolls, tax lists, *etc. etc.*
- Eighteenth Century Sources
  freepages.genealogy.rootsweb.com/~irishancestors/Add18.html
  Covers a wide range of sources
- Nineteenth Century Sources
  freepages.genealogy.rootsweb.com/~irishancestors/Add19.html
  Covers a wide range of sources, including estate records, wills, poor law records, *etc. etc.*
- Guide to Researching Irish Family/Social History in Dundee
  www.fdca.org.uk/irishguide.htm
- Irish Records Index, 1500-1920
  www.ancestry.com/search/rectype/inddbs/4077.htm
  Index to a collection held by the Mormon's Family History Library

3. Libraries, Record Offices and Books

Most of the information sought by genealogists is likely to be found in books and archival sources. The libraries and record offices which hold these resources provide an essential genealogical service, which is unlikely to be replaced by the internet. The value of the latter is in pointing you in the right direction, and helping you to identify the books and records you need to check. Most libraries and record offices now have webpages, listed here. Those which provide internet access to their catalogues are providing a particularly valuable service.

It is impossible here to provide a complete list of library and record office websites likely to be of use to genealogists. Such a list would have to include most public and university libraries, and is outside the scope of this book. However, a number of sites provide extensive listings. Three sites are specifically intended for genealogists:

- Familia: the UK and Ireland's guide to genealogical resources in public libraries
  www.familia.org.uk
- Local Library (Republic of Ireland)
  scripts.ireland.com/ancestor/browse/addresses/librarya__l.htm
  Continued at **/librarym-z.htm**
  List of addresses
- Local Library (Northern Ireland)
  scripts.ireland.com/ancestor/browse/addresses/libraryn.htm

There are also a number of general gateways to library sites:
- CURL: Consortium of University Research Libraries
  www.curl.ac.uk
  Resources of libraries throughout the British Isles

- Libdex: the Library Index. Ireland
  www.libdex.com/country/Ireland.html

- Libdex: the Library Index. Northern Ireland
  www.libdex.com/country/Northern__Ireland.html

For university library catalogues, consult:
- Irish Academic Library Catalogues
  www.may.ie/library/gateway/other__catalogues.shtml
  List

- Hytelnet: 1st Directory of Internet Resources. Library Catalogs: Ireland
  www.lights.com/hytelnet/ie0/ie000.html
  University Libraries

For a union catalogue of 20 UK and Irish university libraries, consult:
- Copac
  www.copac.ac.uk

For record offices, consult:
- Major Repositories
  scripts.ireland.com/ancestor/browse/addresses/major.htm
  List

- Archon Directory
  www.nationalarchives.gov.uk/archon
  Includes lists of repositories in Northern Ireland and the Republic of Ireland

- What's What in Irish Genealogy: Record Repositories
  indigo.ie/~gorry/Reposit.html

Major Institutions

British Library
- The British Library
  www.bl.uk
  General information and public catalogue

- British Library Manuscripts Catalogue
  molcat.bl.uk/
  Includes extensive Irish collection

Family History Library
- Family History Library
  www.familysearch.org
  Library of the Latter Day Saints. Click on 'library' and 'Family History Centers' for a list of branches world-wide (including Ireland)

- LDS films of interest to those studying Co. Longford families
  www3.nbnet.ca/moffatt/ldsfilms.html

- FHC Film and Microfilm
  ahd.exis.net/monaghan/fhc-records.htm
  For Co. Monaghan

Linen Hall Library
- Linen Hall Library, Belfast
  www.linenhall.com
  The leading centre for Irish and local studies in the north of Ireland. Includes catalogue

National Archives of Ireland
- A Guide to the National Archives of Ireland
  homepage.eircom.net/~seanjmurphy/nai/

- National Archives of Ireland
  www.nationalarchives.ie

- National Archives of Ireland: Genealogy
  www.nationalarchives.ie/genealogy/index.html

National Library of Ireland
- National Library of Ireland
  www.nli.ie
  Includes catalogue, pages on 'family history research' in the National Library, details of collections, *etc.*

National Archives [U.K.]
- Irish Genealogy
  www.nationalarchives.gov.uk/researchguidesindex.asp
  Click on title. Resources in the U.K. National Archives.

- National Archives
  www.nationalarchives.gov.uk

Public Record Office of Northern Ireland
- The Public Record Office of Northern Ireland
  www.proni.gov.uk
  Includes details of the extensive records held

Representative Church Body Library
- Representative Church Body Library
  www.ireland.anglican.org/library
  Repository of the archives of the Church of Ireland

Ulster American Folk Park
- The Ulster American Folk Park
  www.folkpark.com
  Includes 'The Centre for Migration Studies', with its library and 'emigration database'

University Libraries
- Boole Library, University College Cork, Ireland: Special Collections
  booleweb.ucc.ie/search/subject/speccol/speccol.htm

- Trinity College Library, Dublin
  www.tcd.ie/library

- National University of Ireland, Maynooth: Library Online
  www.may.ie/library

- University of Ulster Library Services
  www.library.ulster.ac.uk

Public Libraries
Clare
- Clare County Library
  www.clarelibrary.ie
Includes pages on 'Genealogy', 'History', 'Clare County Archives', *etc.*

Cork
- Cork City and County Archives
  www.corkcity.ie/ourservices/rac/archives

Donegal
- Donegal Libraries & Information
  www.donegallibrary.ie/
  Includes pages on 'Donegal Studies' and 'Family History', *etc.*

Dublin
- Dublin City Public Libraries and Archive
  www.dublincity.ie/living__in__the__city/libraries

- Dun Laoghaire-Rathdown County Council Public Library Service: Local History Department
  www.dlrcoco.ie/library/
  Includes library catalogue, and page on 'local history'.

- Fingal County Libraries
  www.iol.ie/~fincolib
  Includes pages on 'Local Studies' and 'County Archives'

Galway
- Galway Public Library
  www.galwaylibrary.ie
  Includes page on 'local archives'

Kerry
- Kerry County Library Local History and Archives Department
  www.kerrycountylibrary.com/
  Click on 'Local History' & 'Archives'.

Kildare
- Kildare Library & Arts Service
  www.kildare.ie/library
  Includes page on 'Local Studies'.

Kilkenny
- Kilkenny County Library
  www.familia.org.uk/services/eire/kilkenny.html

Limerick
- Limerick County Council: Library
  www.lcc.ie/library
  Includes pages on 'Archives' and 'Local studies'.

Longford
- Longford County Library
  www.longford.library.ie
  Click on 'Archives & Local Studies'.

Louth
- Louth County Archives Service
  www.louthcoco.ie/Index.aspx?deptid=18&dpageid=O

- Louth County Archives Service
  www.louthcoco.ie/louthcoco/louth/html/archive.htm

Mayo
- Mayo County Library Local Studies
  www.mayolibrary.ie/index.html

Meath
- Archives and Libraries for Genealogical and Local Historical Research concerning County Meath
  www.angelfire.com/ak2/ashbourne/archives.html

Monaghan
- Monaghan County Council Library: Local History & Genealogy Services
  www.monaghan.ie/library/history.asp

Roscommon
- Roscommon County Library
  www.iol.ie/~roslib/
  Includes page on 'local history'

Tipperary
- Tipperary Libraries: Local Studies Department
  www.tipperarylibraries.ie/local__studies/

Waterford
- Waterford County Library
  www.waterfordcountylibrary.ie/library/web
  Click 'Online resources' for a range of genealogical databases; also 'services' for pages on local studies and family history

- Waterford City Archives
  www.waterfordcity.ie/archives/index.htm

Westmeath
- Westmeath County Council: Library: Local Studies & Archives: Genealogy
  www.westmeathcoco.ie/services/library/genealogy.asp

Wexford
- Wexford Public Library Services
  www.wexford.ie/wex/Departments/Library
Includes pages on 'Archive' and 'Local Studies'

Irish Family History Foundation
This Foundation coordinates a network of government sponsored genealogical research centres which have computerised millions of records. These centres are listed below. The coordinating body is:

- Irish Family History Foundation
  www.irish-roots.net

For listings of the centres, see:
- County Based Genealogical Centres
  www.nationalarchives.ie/genealogy/centres.html

- Local Heritage Centres
  scripts.ireland.com/ancestor/browse/addresses/heritagea-k.htm
  Continued at /heritagel-z.htm

Antrim
- Ulster Historical Foundation
  www.irish-roots.net/antrim-down.asp
  Covers Co. Antrim and Co. Down

Armagh
- Armagh Ancestry
  www.irish-roots.net/armagh.htm

Cavan
- Cavan Genealogy
  www.irish-roots.net/cavan.asp

Clare
- Clare Heritage and Genealogical Centre
  www.clareroots.com

Cork
- Mallow Heritage Centre
  www.irish-roots.net/Cork.htm
  Covers Co. Cork

- Cork City Ancestral Project
  www.irish-roots.net.cork.asp

Donegal
- Donegal Ancestry
  www.donegalancestry.com

Down
See Antrim

Dublin
- Dun Laoghaire Heritage Society
  www.irish-roots.net/dublin-south-dun-laoghaire.asp

- Swords Historical Society
  www.irish-roots.net/dublin-north-fingal.asp

Fermanagh
- Irish World Family History Services
  www.irish-roots.net/fermanagh-tyrone.asp
  Covers Co. Fermanagh and Co. Tyrone

Galway
- East Galway Family History Society
  www.irish-roots.net/galway-east.asp

- Genealogy in Galway in the West of Ireland
  www.irish-roots.net/Galway.htm

- Galway Family History Society West Ltd.
  www.irish-roots.net/galway-west.asp

Kerry
- Killarney Genealogical Centre
  www.goireland.com/Genealogy/Html/counties/Kerry.htm
  Covers Co. Kerry

Kildare
- Kildare Heritage and Genealogy Company
  Kildare.ie/heritage/genealogy

Kilkenny
- Kilkenny Archaeological Society
  www.kilkennyarchaeologicalsociety.ie

Laois
- Laois & Offaly Family History Research Centre
  www.irish-roots.com/laois-offaly.asp

- Irish Midlands Ancestry
  www.irishmidlandsancestry.com
  Covers Laois and Offaly

Leitrim
- Leitrim Genealogy Centre
  homepage.circom.net/%7Eleitrimgenealogy

Limerick
- Limerick Ancestry
  www.irishroots.net/Limerick.htm

Londonderry
- County Derry Londonderry
  www.irish-roots.net/derry.asp

Longford
- Longford Research Centre
  www.irish-roots.net/longford.asp

Louth
See also Meath
- Louth Co. Library
  www.irish-roots.net/louth.asp

Mayo
- Mayo Family History Centres
  mayo.irish-roots.net/mayo/Mayo.htm

Meath
- Meath Heritage Centre
  www.meathroots.com

- Meath-Louth Family Research Centre
  www.irish-roots.net/Louth.htm

Offaly
See Laois

Roscommon
• County Roscommon Heritage and Genalogy Company
  www.roscommonroots.com

Sligo
• County Sligo Heritage and Genealogy Centre
  www.sligoroots.com

Tipperary
• Bru Boru Heritage Centre
  www.irishroots.net/tipperary-south.asp
  Covers South Tipperary

• North Tipperary Genealogy and Heritage Services
  www.irishroots.net/tipperary-north.asp

Tyrone
See Fermanagh

Waterford
• Genealogy Waterford Ireland
  www.iol.ie/~mnoc

Westmeath
• Dun na Si Heritage Centre
  www.irish-roots.net/westmeath.asp
  Covers Co. Westmeath

Wexford
• County Wexford Heritage & Genealogy Society
  homepage.eir.com.net/%7Eyolawexford/genealogy.htm

Wicklow
• Wicklow Family History Centre
  www.irish-roots.net/wicklow.asp

Books

It is vital that the genealogist should be aware of the thousands of published books that may be of assistance in research. They contain far more information than is available on the web. In order to identify them, you need to consult bibliographies. A number are available on the web, and are listed here. Once you have identified the particular books you need, you can find them by checking the library catalogues listed earlier in this chapter.

• Genealogical Publications
  www.nationalarchives.ie/genealogy/publications.html

• Irish Genealogy
  www.acpl.lib.in.us/genealogy/04irish.pdf
  Bibliographic guide from the Allen County Public Library, U.S.A.

• Irish Genealogy
  www.newberry.org/genealogy/irish.html
  Bibliography from the Newberry Library, Chicago

• Sources for Research in Irish Genealogy
  www.loc.gov/rr/genealogy/bib_guid/ireland.html
  Library of Congress bibliography compiled in 1998

• The Irish Ancestral Research Association: Books, Publications and Libraries
  tiara.ie/books.html
  Details of books for sale, libraries, publishers, periodicals, etc.

• Northern Irish References: Ulster Province Family History
  www.rootsweb.com/~fianna/NIR/
  Bibliographic guide, with pages on Co's Antrim, Armagh, Donegal, Down, Fermanagh, Londonderry, Monaghan, and Tyrone

Armagh
• Armagh Books
  www.from-ireland.net/books/armagh.htm
  Bibliography

Donegal
• S. W. Donegal Irish Genealogy & our Irish Heritage
  www.radiks.net/~keving/Donegal/DonegalGen.html
  Includes much bibliographic information.

Longford
- County Longford: a Bibliography
  www.rootsweb.com/~irllog/longbib.htm
  Brief

Sligo
- County Sligo, Ireland: Books
  www.rootsweb.com/~irlsli/books.html
  Lists books with purchasing details

Tipperary
- Tipperary Books: a bibliography
  www.rootsweb.com/~irltip2/tipbib.htm
  Brief

4. Family History Societies

Many Irish family history societies have websites. These generally provide information on the society - names of officers, meetings, membership information, publications, services offered, lists of members' interests, links to other web pages, *etc.* A number of listings of societies are available:

- Family History and Genealogy Societies: Ireland
  www.genuki.org.uk/Societies/Ireland.html

- Family History Societies
  scripts.ireland.com/ancestor/browse/addresses/family.htm
  Brief list, websites not listed

- Federation of Family History Societies: Irish Societies
  www.ffhs.org.uk/General/Members/Ireland.htm
  Lists addresses

- Irish Genealogical Societies and Periodicals / Kyle Betit
  globalgenealogy.com/globalgazette/gazkb/gazkb45.htm

For local history societies, see:
- Local History Societies
  scripts.ireland.com/ancestor/browse/addresses/history.htm
  List

National & Regional Organisations
- Council of Irish Genealogical Organisations
  indigo.ie/~gorry/CIGO.html

- Genealogical Society of Ireland
  www.familyhistory.ie

- Irish Family History Society
  homepage.eircom.net/~ifhs/

- North of Ireland Family History Society
  www.nifhs.org

- Ulster Historical Foundation
  www.ancestryireland.com

Overseas Societies

Australia
- Australian Institute of Genealogical Studies Inc. Scottish / Irish Special Interest Group
  www.aigs.org.au/irscotsig.htm

- Irish Ancestry Group: a service group of the Genealogical Society of Victoria
  www.gsv.org.au/irish.htm

- Western Australian Genealogical Society Inc. Special Interest Group. Irish Group
  www.wags.org.au/groups/sigirish.htm

England
- Irish Genealogical Research Society
  www.igrsoc.org/

- Manchester & Lancashire Family History Society: Irish Ancestry Branch
  www.mlfhs.org.uk
  Click on 'Irish Ancestry Branch'

New Zealand
- New Zealand Society of Genealogists Inc. Irish Interest Group
  www.genealogy.org.nz/sig/irish.html

United States
- Irish Genealogical Society International
  www.irishgenealogical.org
  Based in Minneapolis area, Minnesota

- American Irish Historical Society
  www.aihs.org

- Buffalo Irish Genealogical Society
  www.buffalonet.org/army/bigs.htm

- British Isles Family History Society-U.S.A: Irish Study Group
  www.rootsweb.com/~bifhsusa/study-irish.html

- Irish American Archives Society
  www.wrhs.org/library/template.asp?id=270
  Irish emigrants to Cleveland, Ohio

- The Irish Ancestral Research Association
  www.tiara.ie
  Based in Massachusetts

- Irish Family History Forum
  www.ifhf.org
  Based in New York

- Irish Genealogical Society of Michigan
  www.rootsweb.com/~miigsm/

- Irish Genealogical Society of Wisconsin
  my.execpc.com/~igsw/

- Buffalo Irish Genealogical Society
  www.buffalonet.org/army/bigs.htm

- Irish Palatine Association
  www.irishpalatines.org
  For German migrants to Ireland

Local Organisations

Cork
- Cork Genealogical Society
  homepage.eircom.net/~aocoleman

- Mallow Archaeological & Historical Society
  www.rootsweb.com/~irlmahs/
  For northern Co. Cork

Offaly
- Offaly Historical & Archaeological Society
  www.offalyhistory.com

Roscommon
- County Roscommon Family History Society
  www.geocities.com/Heartland/Pines/7030

Tipperary
- Cumann Staire Chontae Thiobraid Arann / County Tipperary Historical Society
www.tipperarylibraries.ie/ths/index.htm

5. Discussion Groups: Mailing Lists and Newsgroups

Want to ask someone who knows? Then join one of the groups listed here. For general information on mailing lists, visit:

- FAQ: Mailing Lists: What are they for?
helpdesk.rootsweb.com/help/mail1.html

When you join a mailing list, you can send and receive messages from every other member of the group. By way of contrast, you do not have to join the Usenet newsgroups in order to use them; all you need is newsreading software. The two major Irish newsgroups are 'gatewayed' to, and can also be used as, mailing lists. They are:

- **soc.genealogy.ireland**
Gatewayed to Genire (see below)

- **soc.genealogy.surnames.ireland**
Gatewayed to IRL-SURNAMES (see below)

An index to the contents of newsgroups is available at:
- Deja's Usenet Archive
groups.google.com/googlegroups/archive__announce.html

The most comprehensive listing of mailing lists is:
- Genealogy Resources on the Internet: Ireland mailing lists
www.rootsweb.com/~jfuller/gen__mail__country-unk-irl.html

See also
- Genealogy Mailing Lists
www.genuki.org.uk/indexes/MailingLists.html

- The British Isles Gen Web Project: Ireland Related Mailing Lists
www.britishislesgenweb.org/irelandmail.htm

- Mailing Lists
lists.rootsweb.com

General Irish Mailing Lists

- CELTIC QUEST Mailing List
  lists.rootsweb.com/index/intl/IRL/CELTICQUEST.html

- Cousin Connect.com
  www.cousinconnect.com
  International query boards, with separate pages for most Irish counties.

- Fianna Mailing List
  lists.rootsweb.com/index/intl/IRL/FIANNA.html

- Genire Mailing List
  lists.rootsweb.com/index/intl/IRL/GENIRE.html

- Gen-Trivia Ireland
  lists.rootsweb.com/index/intl/IRL/GEN-TRIVIA-IRELAND.html

- Ireland Genealogy
  groups.yahoo.com/group/Y-IRL/

- Ireland GenWeb Mailing List
  lists.rootsweb.com/index/intl/IRL/IrelandGenWeb.html

- Ireland Mailing List
  lists.rootsweb.com/index/intl/IRL/IRELAND.html

- IRELAND-ROLL-CALLS mailing list
  lists.rootsweb.com/index/intl/IRL/IRELAND-ROLL-CALLS.html

- Ireland-Roots Mailing List
  lists.rootsweb.com/index/intl/IRL/IRELAND-ROOTS.html

- Irish Ancestors Group
  groups.yahoo.com/Irishancestorsgroup

- irishancestry
  groups.yahoo.com/group/irishancestry

- IrishGenealogy.com
  groups.yahoo.com/group/IrishGenealogy-com
  Newsletter

- Irish Genealogy on the Net: Ireland
  www.irishgenealogy.net/cp/forum/index.php
  Click on title

- IrishGenes Mailing List
  lists.rootsweb.com/index/intl/IRL/IrishGenes.html

- Shamrock Mailing List
  lists.rootsweb.com/index/intl/IRL/SHAMROCK.html

Irish Overseas Mailing Lists

- Ethnic-Irish Mailing Lists
  lists.rootsweb.com/index/other/Ethnic_Irish/
  Gateway to lists for the Irish overseas

Australia

- Aus-Irish Mailing List
  lists.rootsweb.com/index/other/Ethnic-Irish/AUS-IRISH.html

- Irish Australian
  groups.yahoo.com/group/irishaustralian

Canada

- Ethnic-Irish: Irish-Canadian Mailing List
  lists.rootsweb.com/index/other/Ethnic-Irish/Irish-Canadian.html

- Ethnic Irish: CAN-CHALEUR-BAY-IRISH Mailing List
  lists.rootsweb.com/index/other/Ethnic-Irish/
  CAN-CHALEUR-BAY-IRISH.html

- Can-Montreal-Irish Mailing List
  lists.rootsweb.com/index/other/Ethnic-Irish/
  CAN-MONTREAL-IRISH.html

United States

- IRELAND-ROLL-CALLS Mailing List
  lists.rootsweb.com/index/intl/IRL/IRELAND-ROLL-CALLS.html

- Ireland American Lineages and More
  groups.msn.com/IrelandAmericanLineagesandMore/home.htm

- Ethnic-Irish: IRISH-AMERICAN Mailing List
  lists.rootsweb.com/index/other/Ethnic-Irish/
  IRISH-AMERICAN.html

- Irish American Obituaries
  lists.rootsweb.com/index/other/Ethnic-Irish/
  IRISH-AMERICAN-OBITUARIES.html

- Ethnic Irish: IRISH-IN-CHICAGO Mailing List
lists.rootsweb.com/index/other/Ethnic-Irish/
IRISH-IN-CHICAGO.html

- Ethnic-Irish: IRISH-IN-FLORIDA Mailing List
lists.rootsweb.com/index/other/Ethnic-Irish/
IRISH-IN-FLORIDA.html

- Ethnic Irish: ME-IRISH Mailing List
lists.rootsweb.com/index/other/Ethnic-Irish/**ME-IRISH.html**
Irish in Maine

- Ethnic Irish: IRISH-MI Mailing List
lists.rootsweb.com/index/other/Ethnic-Irish/**IRISH-MI.html**
Irish in Michigan

- Ethic-Irish: IRISH-NEW-YORK-CITY Mailing List
lists.rootsweb.com/index/other/Ethnic-Irish/
IRISH-NEW-YORK-CITY.html

- Ethnic-Irish: NY-IRISH Mailing List
lists.rootsweb.com/index/other/Ethnic-Irish/**NY-IRISH.html**
New York Irish

- Ethnic-Irish: IRISH-NY-TROY Mailing List
lists.rootsweb.com/index/other/Ethnic-Irish/**IRISH-IN-TROY.html**
Irish in Troy, New York

- OH-Cleveland-Irish Mailing List
lists.rootsweb.com/index/other/Ethnic-Irish/
OH-CLEVELAND-IRISH.html

- Ethnic-Irish: IRISH-IN-PENNSYLVANIA Mailing List
lists.rootsweb.com/index/other/Ethnic-Irish/
IRISH-IN-PENNSYLVANIA.html

- Ethnic-Irish: IRISH-IN-PHILADELPHIA Mailing List
lists.rootsweb.com/index/other/Ethnic-Irish/
IRISH-IN-PHILADELPHIA.html

- Ethnic-Irish: IRISH-IN-ST. LOUIS Mailing List
lists.rootsweb.com/index/other/Ethnic-Irish/
IRISH-IN-ST-LOUIS.html

- IA-Irish Mailing List
lists.rootsweb.com/index/other/Ethnic-Irish/**IA-IRISH.html**
For Irish in Iowa

United Kingdom
- Ethnic-Irish: IRISH-IN-UK Mailing List
lists.rootsweb.com/index/other/Ethnic-Irish/**IRISH-IN-UK.html**

- Ethnic Irish: IRISH-IN-COVENTRY Mailing List
lists.rootsweb.com/index/other/Ethnic-Irish/
IRISH-IN-COVENTRY.html

- Ethnic-Irish: IRISH-SCOTS Mailing List
lists.rootsweb.com/index/other/Ethnic-Irish/**IRISH-SCOTS.html**

- SCOTCH-IRISH-CULTURE Mailing List
lists.rootsweb.com/index/intl/NIR/SCOTCH-IRISH-CULTURE.html

Specialist Mailing Lists
- BLACK-IRISH Mailing List
lists.rootsweb.com/index/intl/IRL/BLACK-IRISH.html

- Ireland Book-Discussion Mailing List
lists.rootsweb.com/index/intl/IRL/
IRELAND-BOOK-DISCUSSION.html

- Ireland Cemeteries Mailing List
lists.rootsweb.com/index/intl/IRL/IRELAND-CEMETERIES.html

- IRISH-ADOPTEES-SEARCH Mailing List
lists.rootsweb.com/index/intl/IRL/
IRISH-ADOPTEES-SEARCH.html

- Ireland Book Discussion Mailing List
www.connorsgenealogy.com/books
Includes lookup pages

- IRL-CLANS Mailing List
lists.rootsweb.com/index/intl/IRL/IRL-CLANS.html

- IRISH-DNA Mailing List
lists.rootsweb.com/index/intl/IRL/IRISH-DNA.html

- IRL-PALATINE Mailing List
lists.rootsweb.com/index/intl/IRL/**IRL-PALATINE.html**

- IRL-TOMBSTONE-INSCRIPTIONS Mailing List
  lists.rootsweb.com/index/intl/IRL/
  IRL-TOMBSTONE-INSCRIPTIONS.html

- Irish-Famine Mailing List
  lists.rootsweb.com/index/intl/IRL/IRISH-FAMINE.html

- FENIANS Mailing List
  lists.rootsweb.com/index/intl/IRL/FENIANS.html

- Ireland Obits Mailing List
  lists.rootsweb.com/index/intl/IRL/IRELAND-OBITS.html

- Irish-Adoptees-Search Mailing List
  lists.rootsweb.com/index/intl/IRL/
  IRISH-ADOPTEES-SEARCH.html

- IRL-GEN-MEDIEVAL Mailing List
  lists.rootsweb.com/index/intl/IRL/IRL-GEN-MEDIEVAL.html

- IRL-SURNAMES Mailing List
  lists.rootsweb.com/index/intl/IRL/IRL-SURNAMES.html
  Gatewayed to soc.genealogy.surnames.ireland (see above)

- Scotch-Irish Mailing List
  lists.rootsweb.com/index/intl/NIR/Scotch-Irish.html

- Transcriptions Eire Mailing List
  lists.rootsweb.com/index/intl/IRL/TRANSCRIPTIONS-EIRE.html

Provincial Mailing Lists

Connaught
- IRL-CONNAUGHT Mailing List
  lists.rootsweb.com/index/intl/IRL/IRL-CONNAUGHT.html

Leinster
- IRL-LEINSTER Mailing List
  lists.rootsweb.com/index/intl/IRL/IRL-LEINSTER.html

Ulster/Northern Ireland
- IRL-ulster Mailing List
  lists.rootsweb.com/index/intl/NIR/IRL-ULSTER.html

- Irish Genealogy on the Net: N. Ireland
  www.irishgenealogy.net/cp/forum/index.php
  Click on title. Outside Co. Antrim

- Northern Ireland Gen Web Mailing List
  lists.rootsweb.com/index/intl/NIR/NorthernIrelandGenWeb.html

- Northern Ireland Mailing List
  lists.rootsweb.com/index/intl/NIR/NORTHERN-IRELAND.html

- Unionist-Culture Mailing List
  lists.rootsweb.com/index/intl/NIR/Unionist-Culture.html
  Covers Northern Ireland

- N-Ireland Mailing List
  lists.rootsweb.com/index/intl/NIR/N-IRELAND.html

County & Local Mailing Lists
This listing includes a small number of message/query boards.

Antrim
- IRL-Antrim Mailing List
  lists.rootsweb.com/index/intl/NIR/IRL-ANTRIM.html

- NIR-Antrim Mailing List
  lists.rootsweb.com/index/intl/NIR/NIR-ANTRIM.html

- Irish Genealogy on the Net: Ahoghill
  www.irishgenealogy.net/cp/forum/index.php
  Click on title

- Irish Genealogy on the Net: Ballygally-Glenarm-Cushendall-Ballycastle
  www.irishgenealogy.net/cp/forum/index.php
  Click on title

- IRL-BELFAST-CITY Mailing List
  lists.rootsweb.com/index/intl/IRL/IRL-BELFAST-CITY.html

- IRL-BELFAST-Catholic Mailing List
  lists.rootsweb.com/index/intl/NIR/IRL-Belfast-Catholic.html

- Irish Genealogy on the Net: Belfast - Co. Antrim & Co. Down
  www.irishgenealogy.net/cp/forum/index.php
  Click on title

- Irish Genealogy on the Net: the rest of Co. Antrim
  www.irishgenealogy.net/cp/forum/index.php
  Click on title

- Irish Genealogy on the Net: Ballymena
  www.irishgenealogy.net/cp/forum/index.php
  Click on title

Armagh
- NIR-Armagh Mailing List
  lists.rootsweb.com/index/intl/NIR/NIR-ARMAGH.html

- NIR-Armagh-City Mailing List
  lists.rootsweb.com/index/intl/NIR/NIR-ARMAGH-CITY.html

Carlow
- IRL-CARLOW Mailing List
  lists.rootsweb.com/index/intl/IRL/IRL-CARLOW.html

Cavan
- County Cavan Genealogy Queries
  www.cousinconnect.com/p/a/1100
  Query board

- IRL-CAVAN Mailing List
  lists.rootsweb.com/index/intl/IRL/IRL-CAVAN.html

Clare
- IRL-CLARE Mailing List
  lists.rootsweb.com/index/intl/IRL/IRL-CLARE.html

Cork
- County Cork Ireland Cafe
  groups.yahoo.com/group/countycorkirelandcafe

- County Cork Mailing List
  lists.rootsweb.com/index/intl/IRL/CountyCork.html

- IRL-CORK Mailing List
  lists.rootsweb.com/index/intl/IRL/IRL-CORK.html

- IRL-CORK-CITY Mailing List
  lists.rootsweb.com/index/intl/IRL/IRL-CORK-CITY.html

- Beara Mailing List
  lists.rootsweb.com/index/intl/IRL/Beara.html
  Covers the Berehaven Peninsula, Co's Cork and Kerry

- IRL-CORK-MALLOW Mailing List
  lists.rootsweb.com/index/intl/IRL/IRL-CORK-MALLOW.html

Donegal
- County Donegal Genealogy
  groups.yahoo.com/group/CountyDonegalGenealogy/

- Donegal, Ireland Connection Boards
  www.geocities.com/Heartland/Estates/6587/Donconnect.html
  List of bulletin boards, *etc.*

- Carndonagh/Inishowen Message Board
  users2.cgiforme.com/carn/cfmboard.html

- Donegal Mailing List
  www.rootsweb.com/~irldon2/genealogy/maillist__info.htm

- IRL-DONEGAL Mailing List
  lists.rootsweb.com/index/intl/IRL/IRL-DONEGAL.html

- IRL-CO-DONEGAL Mailing List
  lists.rootsweb.com/index/intl/IRL/IRL-CO-DONEGAL.html

- IRL-DONEGAL-ROLLCALL Mailing List
  lists.rootsweb.com/index/intl/IRL/
  IRL-DONEGAL-ROLLCALL.html

- Donegaleire Mailing List
  lists.rootsweb.com/index/intl/IRL/DONEGALEIRE.html

- IRL-ARRANMORE Mailing List
  lists.rootsweb.com/index/intl/IRL/IRL-ARRANMORE.html

Down
- NIR-DOWN Mailing List
  lists.rootsweb.com/index/intl/NIR/NIR-DOWN.html

Dublin
- IRL-DUBLIN Mailing List
  lists.rootsweb.com/index/intl/IRL/IRL-DUBLIN.html

- IRL-DUBLIN-CITY Mailing List
  lists.rootsweb.com/index/intl/IRL/IRL-DUBLIN-CITY.html

Fermanagh
- Fermanagh Gold Mailing List
  lists.rootsweb.com/index/intl/NIR/FERMANAGH-GOLD.html

- Fermanagh Mailing List
  lists.rootsweb.com/index/intl/NIR/FERMANAGH.html

- IRL-Fermanagh
  lists.rootsweb.com/index/intl/NIR/IRL-FERMANAGH.html

Galway
- County Galway Surname Queries
  www.rootsweb.com/~irlgal/surnames.htm
  Message Board

- IRL-GALWAY Mailing List
  lists.rootsweb.com/index/intl/IRL/IRL-GALWAY.html

- IRL-ARAN-ISLANDS Mailing List
  lists.rootsweb.com/index/intl/IRL/IRL-ARAN-ISLANDS.html

- IRL-ARAN-ISLANDS Mailing List
  lists.rootsweb.com/index/intl/IRL/IRL-ARAN-ISLANDS.html

- IRE-GALWAY-INISHBOFIN Mailing List
  lists.rootsweb.com/index/intl/IRL/IRE-GALWAY-INISHBOFIN.html

- LETTERMULLEN-GALWAY Mailing List
  lists.rootsweb.com/index/intl/IRL/
  LETTERMULLEN-GALWAY.html

- IRL-GALWAY-WOODFORD Mailing List
  lists.rootsweb.com/index/intl/IRL/IRL-GALWAY-WOODFORD.html

Kerry See also Cork
- IRL-KERRY Mailing List
  lists.rootsweb.com/index/intl/IRL/IRL-KERRY.html

- Kerry Kin
  groups.yahoo.com/group/kerrykin

- IRL-KIL-CASTLECOMER Mailing List
  lists.rootsweb.com/index/intl/IRL/IRL-KIL-CASTLECOMER.html

Kildare
- IRL-CO-KILDARE Mailing Lists
  lists.rootsweb.com/index/intl/IRL/IRL-CO-KILDARE.html

- IRL-KILDARE Mailing List
  lists.rootsweb.com/index/intl/IRL/IRL-KILDARE.html

Kilkenny
- IRL-KILKENNY Mailing List
  lists.rootsweb.com/index/intl/IRL/IRL-KILKENNY.html

- KILKENNY Mailing List
  lists.rootsweb.com/index/intl/IRL/KILKENNY.html

Laois
- IRL-LAOIS Mailing List
  lists.rootsweb.com/index/int/IRL/IRL-LAOIS.html

- IRL-LEIX Mailing List
  lists.rootsweb.com/index/intl/IRL/IRL-LEIX.html

Leitrim
- IRL-LEITRIM Mailing List
  lists.rootsweb.com/index/intl/IRL/IRL-LEITRIM.html

- The Leitrim-Roscommon Genealogy Bulletin Board
  www.leitrim-roscommon.com/bbs

Limerick
- IRL-LIMERICK Mailing List
  lists.rootsweb.com/index/intl/IRL/IRL-LIMERICK.html

Londonderry
- NIR-Derry Mailing List
  lists.rootsweb.com/index/intl/NIR/NIR-DERRY.html

Longford
- IRL-LONGFORD Mailing List
  lists.rootsweb.com/index/intl/IRL/IRL-LONGFORD.html

Louth
- IRL-LOUTH Mailing List
  lists.rootsweb.com/index/intl/IRL/IRL-LOUTH.html

Mayo
- IRL-MAYO Mailing List
  lists.rootsweb.com/index/intl/IRL/IRL-MAYO.html

- MAYO Mailing List
  lists.rootsweb.com/index/intl/IRL/MAYO.html

- IRL-MAYO-BOHOLA Mailing List
  lists.rootsweb.com/index/intl/IRL/IRL-MAYO-BOHOLA.html

- IRL-MAYO-CLAREMORRIS Mailing List
  lists.rootsweb.com/index/intl/IRL/
  IRL-MAYO-CLAREMORRIS.html

- IRL-MAYO-KILKELLY Mailing List
  lists.rootsweb.com/index/intl/IRL/IRL-MAYO-KILKELLY.html

- IRL-MAYO-KILTIMAGH Mailing List
  lists.rootsweb.com/index/intl/IRL/IRL-MAYO-KILTIMAGH.html

- IRL-MAYO-KINAFFE-SWINFORD Mailing List
  lists.rootsweb.com/index/intl/IRL/
  IRL-MAYO-KINAFFE-SWINFORD.html

- IRL-MAYO-KNOCK Mailing List
  lists.rootsweb.com/index/intl/IRL/IRL-MAYO-KNOCK.html

- IRL-LOUISBURGH mailing list
  lists.rootsweb.com/index/intl/IRL/IRL-LOUISBURGH.html
  In Co. Mayo

- IRL-MAYO-MIDFIELD Mailing List
  lists.rootsweb.com/index/intl/IRL/IRL-MAYO-MIDFIELD.html

Meath
- IRL-MEATH Mailing List
  lists.rootsweb.com/index/intl/IRL/IRL-MEATH.html

Monaghan
- IRL-MONAGHAN Mailing List
  lists.rootsweb.com/index/intl/IRL/IRL-MONAGHAN.html

Munster
- IRL-MUNSTER Mailing List
  lists.rootsweb.com/index/intl/IRL/IRL-MUNSTER.html

Offaly
- IRL-OFFALY Mailing List
  lists.rootsweb.com/index/intl/IRL/IRL-OFFALY.html

Roscommon
See also Leitrim
- IRL-ROSCOMMON Mailing List
  lists.rootsweb.com/index/intl/IRL/IRL-ROSCOMMON.html

- Roscommon Mailing List
  lists.rootsweb.com/index/intl/IRL/ROSCOMMON.html

- IRL-BALLYKILCLINE Mailing List
  lists.rootsweb.com/index/intl/IRL/IRL-BALLYKILCLINE.html

Sligo
- IRL-SLIGO Mailing List
  lists.rootsweb.com/index/intl/IRL/IRL-SLIGO.html

- IRL-BALLYKILCLINE Mailing Lists
  lists.rootsweb.com/index/intl/IRL/IRL-BALLYKILCLINE.html

Tipperary
- Co. Tipperary Mailing List
  lists.rootsweb.com/index/intl/IRL/CoTipperary.html

- IRL-TIPPERARY Mailing List
  lists.rootsweb.com/index/intl/IRL/IRL-TIPPERARY.html
- IRL-tIP-KILNAMANAGH Mailing List
  lists.rootsweb.com/index/intl/IRL/IRL-TIP-KILNAMANAGH.html

Tyrone
- Co. Tyrone, Ireland, Mailing List
  lists.rootsweb.com/index/intl/NIR/CoTyroneIreland.html
- IRL-TYRONE Mailing List
  lists.rootsweb.com/index/intl/NIR/IRL-TYRONE.html
- NIR-Tyrone Mailing List
  lists.rootsweb.com/index/intl/NIR/NIR-TYRONE.html

Waterford
- IRL-WATERFORD Mailing List
  lists.rootsweb.com/index/intl/IRL/IRL-WATERFORD.html
- Waterford Mailing List
  lists.rootsweb.com/index/intl/IRL/WATERFORD.html

Westmeath
- IRL-WESTMEATH Mailing List
  lists.rootsweb.com/index/intl/IRL/IRL-WESTMEATH.html

Wexford
- IRL-WEXFORD Mailing List
  lists.rootsweb.com/index/intl/IRL/IRL-WEXFORD.html
- Wexford Mailing List
  lists.rootsweb.com/index/intl/IRL/WEXFORD.html
- IRL-WEX-ENNISCORTHY Mailing List
  lists.rootsweb.com/index/intl/IRL/IRL-WEX-ENNISCORTHY.html

Wicklow
- IRL-WICKLOW Mailing List
  lists.rootsweb.com/index/intl/IRL/IRL-WICKLOW.html

6. Message/Query Boards

A number of websites offer you the opportunity to post messages / queries on the site itself. For a listing of such sites visit:

- Queries and Message Boards
  www.CyndisList.com/queries.htm

A number of sites offer boards for every Irish county. A small number of county boards are listed in the previous chapter. The main boards (which include many county boards not separately listed) are:

- Genforum: Ireland: Regions
  genforum.genealogy.com/ireland/regions.html
- British Isles GenWeb Project: Ireland Data Boards
  www.irelandgenweb.com/query.html
- [Message Boards]: Ireland
  boards.ancestry.com
  Click on 'United Kingdom and Ireland', and on 'Ireland'. Boards for every Irish county
- CAORA
  www.caora.net/
  Collection of message boards for every county, *etc.*

A variety of forums are available at:
- Irish Genealogy on the Net & Forum Index
  www.irishgenealogy.net/cp/forum/index.php

General Message Boards
- The Information About Ireland Site Genealogy Forum
  www.ireland-information.com/board/wwwboard.html
- Ireland Genealogy Forum
  genforum.genealogy.com/ireland/
- Ireland Genealogy Message Board
  www.voy.com/43747/

- Irish Ancestry
  groups.yahoo.com/group/irishancestry2
- Irish Emigrant Message Board
  www.theirishemigrant.com/Board/default.asp
- Irish Ancestral Pages
  groups.msn.com/IrishAncestralPages
- Irish Family History
  groups.yahoo.com/group/irishfamilyhistory
- Irish Genealogy
  groups.yahoo.com/group/irish-genealogy
- Irish Genealogy
  www.myirishancestry.com
  Click on 'Forums'
- Irish Origins
  groups.msn.com/IrishOrigins
- Irish Relatives
  groups.msn.com/IrishRelatives

7. County Pages

A great deal of information is to be found on county pages. A number of private individuals have created their own county pages, but four organisations have provided pages for every Irish county. The *Irish Times* sites provide the most useful introductory information, but have few links. *Genuki* concentrates attention on primary historical information, rather than on-going and completed research. *Genweb* has some similar information but also includes query boards for each county, and has more information on current and completed research. *Fianna* sites offer a wide range of general information on resources, with many links. *From Ireland* county sites include information under standard headings such as 'gravestones', 'journals', 'religious records', 'links', *etc.*

For a listing of county websites on Rootsweb, see:
- Ireland and Northern Ireland
  www.rootsweb.com/~websites/international/uk.html#ireland

For Northern Ireland, see:
- The Northern Ireland Online Genealogy Centre
  www.nireland.com/genealogy
  Introductory pages
- Northern Ireland Research: Selected Resources
  globalgenealogy.com/globalgazette/gazkb/gazkb60.htm
- The Province of Ulster
  scripts.ireland.com/ancestor/browse/counties/ulster/

Antrim
- Antrim: From Ireland
  www.from-ireland.net/contents/antrimcont.htm

- County Antrim: Fianna's County Page
  www.rootsweb.com/~fianna/county/antrim.html

- Co. Antrim: Northern Ireland GenWeb
  www.rootsweb.com/~nirantri/

- County Antrim, Ireland: Ireland Genealogical Projects
  www.geocities.com/Heartland/Flats/4612/antrim.html

- Genuki Co. Antrim
  www.genuki.org.uk/big/irl/ANT

- Irish Ancestors: County Antrim
  scripts.ireland.com/ancestor/browse/counties/ulster/index__an.htm

- Bann Valley Genealogy
  www.4qd.org/bann/index.html
  Border of Co. Antrim & Co. Londonderry

Armagh
- Armagh: From Ireland
  www.from-ireland.net/contents/armaghconts.htm

- Co. Armagh: Ireland Genealogy Projects
  www.rootsweb.com/~nirarm2

- County Armagh: Fianna County Page
  www.rootsweb.com/~fianna/county/armagh.html

- Genuki Co. Armagh
  www3.ns.sympatico.ca/acauston/genuki/ARM/index.html

- County Armagh: Irish Ancestors
  scripts.ireland.com/ancestor/browse/counties/ulster/index__ar.htm

Carlow
- Carlow County Ireland Genealogical Projects
  www.rootsweb.com/~irlcar2/

- County Carlow: Fianna County Page
  www.rootsweb.com/~fianna/county/carlow.html

- Carlow: From Ireland
  www.from-ireland.net/contents/carlcont.htm

- County Carlow Ireland Gen Web
  www.rootsweb.com/~irlcar/

- Genuki Co. Carlow
  www.genuki.org.uk/big/irl/CAR/

- County Carlow: Irish Ancestors
  scripts.ireland.com/ancestor/browse/counties/leinster/index__ca.htm

Cavan
- Cavan: From Ireland
  www.from-ireland.net/contents/cavancont.htm

- County Cavan: Fianna's County Page
  www.rootsweb.com/~fianna/county/cavan.html

- [Co. Cavan: Genweb]
  www.rootsweb.com/~irlcav2/cavan.html

- Co. Cavan, Ireland, Research Site
  freepages.genealogy.rootsweb.com/~adrian/Cavan.htm

- Genuki Co. Cavan
  www.sierratel.com/colinf/genuki/CAV

- County Cavan. Irish Ancestors
  scripts.ireland.com/ancestor/browse/counties/ulster/index__ca.htm

- Al Beagan's Genealogy Notes of Co. Cavan
  members.tripod.com/~Al__Beagan/tcavan.htm
  Includes many notes on parishes.

Clare
- Clare: From Ireland
  www.from-ireland.net/contents/clareconts.htm

- County Clare
  www.rootsweb.com/~irlcla/

- County Clare: Fianna County Page
  www.rootsweb.com/~fianna/county/clare.html

- County Clare, Ireland Gen Web Project
  www.rootsweb.com/~irlcla2/

- Genuki Co. Clare
  home.pacbell.net/nymets11/genuki/CLA

- County Clare, Ireland
  www.connorsgenealogy.com/clare

- County Clare: Irish Ancestors
  scripts.ireland.com/ancestor/browse/counties/munster/index_cl.htm

Cork
- Cork
  www.from-ireland.net/contents/corkcontents.htm

- Cork
  freepages.genealogy.rootsweb.com/~nyirish/CORK%20index
  Includes extracts from various sources

- Cork Ireland Genweb
  www.cmcrp.net/corkigp

- County Cork
  myhome.ispdr.net.au/~mgrogan/cork/ire.cork.htm
  Gateway to Co. Cork sites on Rootsweb

- County Cork: Fianna County Page
  www.rootsweb.com/~fianna/county/corkcontents.html

- County Cork Ireland Gen Web Project
  www.rootsweb.com/~irlcor

- Genuki Co. Cork
  www.genuki.org.uk/big/irl/COR/

- County Cork: Irish Ancestors
  scripts.ireland.com/ancestor/browse/counties/munster/index_co.htm

- Ginni Swanton's Web Site
  www.ginnisw.com/
  Includes transcripts and indexes etc. of many sources for Co. Cork

Donegal
- County Donegal: Fianna County Page
  www.rootsweb.com/~fianna/county/donegal.html

- County Donegal Ireland Gen Web
  www.rootsweb.com/~irldon

- Donegal. From Ireland
  www.from-ireland.net/contents/donegalconts.htm

- Genuki Co. Donegal
  www.genuki.org.uk/big/irl/DON/

- County Donegal: Irish Times
  scripts.ireland.com/ancestor/browse/counties/ulster/index_do.htm

- Donegal: Ireland Genealogical Project
  www.rootsweb.com/~irldon2/index.htm

- Donegal, Ireland
  freepages.genealogy.rootsweb.com/~donegaleire/Doncontent.html

- Donegal Resources held by the L.D.S.
  freepages.genealogy.rootsweb.com/~donegal/ldsrec.htm

Down
- County Down: Ireland Genealogy Projects
  www.rootsweb.com/~nirdow2/

- Down: From Ireland
  www.from-ireland.net/contents/downconts.htm

- County Down: Fianna County Page
  www.rootsweb.com/~fianna/county/down.html

- County Down
  www.rootsweb.com/~nirdow/
  Gen Web site

- Genuki Co. Down
  www.genuki.org.uk/big/irl/DOW/

- County Down: Irish Ancestors
  scripts.ireland.com/ancestor/browse/counties/ulster/index_dn.htm

- County Down, Northern Ireland, Genealogy
  www.caora.net
  Searchable databases of the Flax Grants (1796), Tithe Record (1820-1830's), Griffiths Valuation (1863), and Census summaries (1901); also message board, chat room, etc.

- Raymonds County Down Website
  www.raymondscountydownwebsite.com/

- Ros Davies' Co. Down, Ireland, Genealogy Research Site
  freepages.genealogy.rootsweb.com/~rosdavies

- Newry, Donaghmore, Loughbrickland & Banbridge Genealogy Site
  freepages.genealogy.rootsweb.com/~donaghmore1

Dublin

- Dublin: From Ireland
  www.from-ireland.net/contents/dublincontents.htm

- County Dublin: Fianna County Page
  www.rootsweb.com/~fianna/county/dublin.html

- County Dublin Ireland Gen Web Project
  www.rootsweb.com/~irldub

- County Dublin, Ireland: Ireland Genealogical Projects
  www.rootsweb.com/~irldubli/

- Genuki Co. Dublin
  www.genuki.org.uk/big/irl/DUB/

- County Dublin: Irish Ancestors
  scripts.ireland.com/ancestor/browse/counties/leinster/index__du.htm

Fermanagh

- County Fermanagh: Fianna County Page
  www.rootsweb.com/~fianna/county/fermanagh.html

- County Fermanagh Northern Ireland Gen Web
  www.rootsweb.com/~nirfer/

- County Fermanagh: Irish Times
  scripts.ireland.com/ancestor/browse/counties/ulster/index__fe.htm

- Fermanagh: From Ireland
  www.from-ireland.net/contents/fermanconts.htm

- Fermanagh: Ireland Genealogy Projects
  www.rootsweb.com/~nirfer2/

- Genuki Co. Fermanagh
  www.genuki.org.uk/big/irl/FER/

Galway

- Galway
  freepages.genealogy.rootsweb.com/~nyirish/GALWAY%20index
  Includes extracts from various sources

- Galway: From Ireland
  www.from-ireland.net/contents/galwayconts.htm

- County Galway: Fianna County Page
  www.rootsweb.com/~fianna/county/galway.html

- Co. Galway Gen Web
  www.rootsweb.com/~irlgal/Galway.html

- County Galway: Ireland Genealogy Projects
  www.rootsweb.com/~irlgal2

- Genuki Co. Galway
  www.genuki.org.uk/big/irl/GAL/

- County Galway: Irish Times
  scripts.ireland.com/ancestor/browse/counties/connacht/index__ga.htm

Kerry

- Kerry: from Ireland
  www.from-ireland.net/contents/kerrycontents.htm

- County Kerry: Fianna County Page
  www.rootsweb.com/~fianna/county/kerry.html

- Co. Kerry Genealogy
  www.rootsweb.com/~irlker
  Genweb site

- Genuki Co. Kerry
  homepage.eircom.net/~dinglemaps/genuki/KER/index.html

- County Kerry: Irish Ancestors
  scripts.ireland.com/ancestor/browse/counties/munster/index__ke.htm

- Finding your Ancestors in Kerry
  www.rootsweb.com/~irlker/find.html
  Introduction

- Kerry Online Records
  www.rootsweb.com/~irlker/records.html
  Links page

- A Dingle, Co. Kerry, Ireland Genealogical Helper
  members.aol.com/waterlilys/

Kildare
- County Kildare: Fianna County Page
  www.rootsweb.com/~fianna/county/kildare.htm

- Co. Kildare, Ireland: Ireland Genealogy Projects
  www.rootsweb.com/~irlkid

- Genuki Co. Kildare
  www.genuki.org.uk/big/irl/KID/

- County Kildare: Irish Ancestors
  scripts.ireland.com/ancestry/browse/counties/leinster/index__ke.htm

- Kildare: From Ireland
  www.from-ireland.net/contents/kilcont.htm

Kilkenny
- County Kilkenny: Fianna County Page
  www.rootsweb.com/~fianna/county/kilkenny.html

- County Kilkenny Genealogy and History
  www.rootsweb.com/~irlkik

- County Kilkenny Genealogy: Ireland Genealogy Projects
  www.rootsweb.com/~irlkik2/

- Genuki Co. Kilkenny
  www.genuki.org.uk/big/irl/KIK/

- County Kilkenny: Irish Ancestors
  scripts.ireland.com/ancestor/browse/counties/leinster/index__ki.htm

- Kilkenny. From Ireland
  www.from-ireland.net/contents/kilkenconts.htm

Laois
- County Laois (Queen's, Leix)
  www.rootsweb.com/~fianna/county/laois.html

- County Leix/Laois
  www.rootsweb.com/~irllex
  Genweb page

- County Laois (Leix), formerly Queen's County Ireland GenWeb Project
  www.rootsweb.com/~irllao

- Genuki Co. Laois (Queen's)
  www.genuki.org.uk/big/irl/LEX

- County Laois: Irish Ancestors
  scripts.ireland.com/ancestor/browse/counties/leinster/index__la.htm

- Laois (Leix, Queen's County): From Ireland
  www.from-ireland.net/contents/laoisconts.htm

Leitrim
- Leitrim: From Ireland
  www.from-ireland.net/contents/leitrimconts.htm

- County Leitrim: Fianna County Page
  www.rootsweb.com/~fianna/county/leitrim.html

- Co. Leitrim: The Ireland Gen Web Project
  www.irelandgenweb.com/~irlleitr

- County Leitrim: Ireland Genealogical Project
  www.rootsweb.com/~irllet

- Genuki Co. Leitrim
  www.genuki.org.uk/big/irl/LET

- County Leitrim: Irish Ancestors
  scripts.ireland.com/ancestor/browse/counties/connacht/index__le.htm

- Leitrim-Roscommon Genealogy Web Site
  www.leitrim-roscommon.com/

Limerick

- County Limerick, Ireland
  www.connorsgenealogy.com/LIM/index.htm

- County Limerick: Fianna County Page
  www.rootsweb.com/~fianna/county/limerick.html

- County Limerick Genealogy
  www.rootsweb.com/~irllimer
  Gen Web site

- County Limerick Genealogy
  www.countylimerickgenealogy.com

- Genuki Co. Limerick
  home.pacbell.net/nymets11/genuki/LIM/

- County Limerick: Irish Ancestors
  scripts.ireland.com/ancestor/browse/counties/munster/index__li.htm

- County Limerick Genealogy
  www.rootsweb.com/~irllimer
  Genweb site

- Limerick: From Ireland
  www.from-ireland.net/contents/limerickconts.htm

Londonderry

See also Antrim

- County Londonderry: Fianna County Page
  www.rootsweb.com/~fianna/county/derry.html

- The Londonderry, Northern Ireland Gen Web Project
  www.rootsweb.com/~nirldy

- Londonderry (Derry): From Ireland
  www.from-ireland.net/contents/londerryconts.htm

- County Londonderry Northern Ireland: Ireland Genealogy Projects
  www.rootsweb.com/~nirldy2/

- Genuki Co. Londonderry
  www.genuki.org.uk/big/irl/LDY/

- County Derry: Irish Ancestors
  scripts.ireland.com/ancestor/browse/counties/ulster/index__de.htm

Longford

- County Longford: Fianna County Page
  www.rootsweb.com/~fianna/county/longford.html

- County Longford, Ireland
  www.rootsweb.com/~irllog2
  Genweb page

- County Longford: Irish Ancestors
  scripts.ireland.com/ancestor/browse/counties/leinster/index__lo.htm

- The Genealogy of County Longford, Ireland
  www.rootsweb.com/~irllog
  I.G.P. site

- Genuki Co. Longford
  www.genuki.org.uk/big/irl/LOG

- Longford: From Ireland
  www.from-ireland.net/contents/longforconts.htm

- Longford Roots
  www.longfordroots.com
  Click on 'records' for various databases

- Edgeworthstown Parish Scrapbook
  www.mostrim.org/Scrapbook/
  Includes various lists, e.g. famine victims 1847

Louth

- County Louth: Fianna's County Page
  www.rootsweb.com/~fianna/county/louth.html

- County Louth: Ireland Genealogy Projects
  www.rootsweb.com/~irllou/

- County Louth, Ireland, Genealogical Sources
  www.jbhall.freeservers.com
  Includes many name lists

- County Louth Ireland Genweb Project
  www.irelandgenweb.com/Louth/louth.html

- County Louth: Irish Ancestors
  scripts.ireland.com/ancestor/browse/counties/leinster.index__lh.htm

- Genuki Co. Louth
  www.genuki.org.uk/big/irl/LOU

- Louth: From Ireland
  www.from-ireland.net/contents/louthcontents.htm

Mayo
- County Mayo: Fianna County Page
  www.rootsweb.com/~fianna/county/mayo.html

- County Mayo: Ireland Genealogy Projects
  www.rootsweb.com/~irlmay/

- County Mayo: the Ireland Genweb Project
  www.rootsweb.com/~irlmayo

- Genuki Co. Mayo
  www.genuki.org.uk/big/irl/MAY/

- County Mayo: Irish Times
  scripts.ireland.com/ancestor/browse/counties/connacht/
  index__ma.htm

- County Mayo, Ireland, Genealogy
  www.geocities.com/Heartland/Acres/4031/mayo.html

- Mayo: From Ireland
  www.from-ireland.net/contents/mayoconts.htm

Meath
- Co. Meath: Irish Ancestors
  scripts.ireland.com/ancestor/browse/counties/leinster/index__me.htm

- County Meath Fianna County Page
  www.rootsweb.com/~fianna/county/meath.html

- County Meath, Republic of Ireland: Ireland Genealogy Projects
  www.rootsweb.com/~irlmea/

- Genuki Co. Meath
  www.genuki.org.uk/big/irl/MEA

- County Meath Ireland Genealogy Project
  www.rootsweb.com/~irlmea2

- Meath: From Ireland
  www.from-ireland.net/contents/meathconts.htm

Monaghan
- County Monaghan: Fianna's County Page
  www.rootsweb.com/~fianna/county/monaghan.html

- Co. Monaghan Ireland Gen Web
  www.rootsweb.com/~irlmog2/

- County Monaghan: Ireland Genealogy Project
  www.rootsweb.com/~irlmog/

- Genuki Co. Monaghan
  www.genuki.org.uk/big/irl/MOG/

- County Monaghan: Irish Ancestors
  scripts.ireland.com/ancestor/browse/counties/ulster/index__mo.htm

- Monaghan: From Ireland
  www.from-ireland.net/contents/monaghanconts.htm

- Monaghan: the County
  www.exis.net/ahd/monaghan/default.htm
  ahd.exis.net/monaghan/

Offaly
- County Offaly (King's): Fianna County Page
  www.rootsweb.com/~fianna/county/offaly.html

- County Offaly Ireland Gen Web Project
  www.rootsweb.com/~irloff2

- Genuki Co. Offaly (King's Co.)
  www.genuki.org.uk/big/irl/OFF/

- County Offaly: Irish Ancestors
  scripts.ireland.com/ancestor/browse/counties/leinster/index__of.htm

- Offaly (King's County)
  www.from-ireland.net/contents/offalyconts.htm

- Offaly, Ireland: King's County
  www.geocities.com/Heartland/Flats/4612/offaly.html

Roscommon

See also Leitrim

- The County Roscommon Database
  www.rootsweb.com/~irlros/

- County Roscommon: Fianna County Page
  www.rootsweb.com/~fianna/county/roscommon.html

- Co. Roscommon Ireland Gen Web Project
  www.rootsweb.com/~irlrosco/

- Genuki Co. Roscommon
  www.genuki.org.uk/big/irl/ROS

- County Roscommon: Irish Ancestors
  scripts.ireland.com/ancestor/browse/counties/connacht/index__ro.htm

- Roscommon: From Ireland
  www.from-ireland.net/contents/roscommconts.htm

Sligo

- County Sligo: Fianna County Page
  www.rootsweb.com/~fianna/county/sligo.html

- Sligo County, Ireland, Genealogy Website
  www.rootsweb.com/~irlsli

- County Sligo, Ireland: Ireland Genealogy Projects
  www.rootsweb.com/~irlsli2/

- Genuki Co. Sligo
  www.genuki.org.uk/big/irl/SLI

- County Sligo: Irish Ancestors
  scripts.ireland.com/ancestor/browse/counties/connaught/index__sl.htm

- Sligo: From Ireland
  www.from-ireland.net/contents/sligoconts

Tipperary

- County Tipperary: Fianna County Page
  www.rootsweb.com/~fianna/county/tipperary.html

- Co. Tipperary: The Ireland Gen Web Project
  www.rootsweb.com/~irltip/tipperary.htm

- County Tipperary, Ireland
  www.connorsgenealogy.com/tipp/

- County Tipperary, Ireland Genealogy
  www.rootsweb.com/~irltip2/

- Genuki Co. Tipperary
  home.pacbel.net/nymets11/TIP

- County Tipperary: Irish Ancestors
  scripts.ireland.com/ancestor/browse/counties/munster/index__ti.htm

- Tipperary: From Ireland
  www.from-ireland.net/contents/tipperconts.htm

- Tipperary, Ireland: Genealogies & Cemeteries
  www.geocities.com/luanndevries/
  Collection of sources, extracts and indexes

- Genealogical Research: Clogheen & District
  www.iol.ie/~clogheen/
  Introduction to parish sources. Click on 'People' and 'Roots'

Tyrone

- County Tyrone: Fianna's County Page
  www.rootsweb.com/~Fianna/county/tyrone.html

- County Tyrone Northern Ireland Gen Web
  www.rootsweb.com/~nirtyr

- Co. Tyrone Genealogy
  freepages.genealogy.rootsweb.com/~tyrone/

- Genuki Co. Tyrone
  www.genuki.org.uk/big/irl/TYR/

- County Tyrone: Irish Ancestors
  scripts.ireland.com/ancestor/browse/counties/ulster/index__ty.htm

- Tyrone: From Ireland
  www.from-ireland.net/contents/tyroneconts.htm

- Tyrone: Ireland Genealogy Projects
  www.rootsweb.com/~nirtyr3/

Waterford
- County Waterford: Fianna's County Page
  www.rootsweb.com/~fianna/county/waterford.html

- County Waterford Genealogy
  www.rootsweb.com/~irlwat2/

- County Waterford: The Ireland Gen Web Project
  www.rootsweb.com/~irlwat

- County Waterford: Irish Ancestors
  scripts.ireland.com/ancestor/browse/counties/munster/index__wa.htm

- Genuki Co. Waterford
  www.genuki.org.uk/big/irl/WAT

- Waterford: From Ireland
  www.from-ireland.net/contents/waterfordconts.htm

Westmeath
- County Westmeath: Fianna's County Page
  www.rootsweb.com/~fianna/county/westmeath.html

- Westmeath Ireland: Genealogy
  www.rootsweb.com/~irlwem2/

- Genuki Co. Westmeath
  www.genuki.org.uk/big/irl/WEM

- Westmeath: From Ireland
  www.from-ireland.net/contents/westmeathconts.htm

- Westmeath: Part of the World Gen Web Project
  www.rootsweb.com/~irlwem

- County Westmeath: Irish Ancestors
  scripts.ireland.com/ancestor/browse.counties/leinster/index__we.htm

Wexford
- County Wexford: Fianna's County Page
  www.rootsweb.com/~fianna/county/wexford.html

- Genuki Co. Wexford
  www.genuki.org.uk/big/irl/WEX/

- County Wexford: Ireland Gen Web
  www.rootsweb.com/~irlwex

- County Wexford: Irish Ancestors
  scripts.ireland.com/ancestor/browse/counties/leinster/index__wd.htm

- Ireland, County Wexford: Ireland Genealogical Project
  users.rootsweb.com/~irlwex2/

- [Wexford]
  freepages.genealogy.rootsweb.com/~nyirish/ WEXFORD%20%20Index.html
  Includes extracts from various sources

- Wexford: From Ireland
  www.from-ireland.net/contents/wexfordconts.htm

Wicklow
- County Wicklow: Fianna's County Page
  www.rootsweb.com/~fianna/county/wicklow.html

- Co. Wicklow
  www.rootsweb.com/~irlwic/
  Genweb page

- Ireland Genealogical Project: County Wicklow Page
  www.rootsweb.com/~irlwic2/

- County Wicklow: Irish Ancestors
  scripts.ireland.com/ancestor/browse/counties/leinster/index__wi.htm

- Genuki Co. Wicklow
  www.genuki.org.uk/big/irl/WIC/

- Wicklow: From Ireland
  www.from-ireland.net/contents/wicklowconts.htm

8. Surnames

The Internet is an invaluable aid for those who want to make contact with others researching the same surname. There are innumerable lists of surname interests, family web-sites, and surname mailing lists. The two latter categories will not be listed here; they are far too numerous for a book of this length, and many are international in scope rather than purely Irish. Such sites may be found through the gateways listed below.

For general guidance on finding surname information on the web, consult:

- Finding Surname Interests
  www.hawgood.co.uk/finding.htm
  General discussion of surnames on the web.

See also:
- Researching Irish Names
  www.rootsweb.com/~fianna/surname/
  General guidance on using surname lists with many links.

Surname Web Pages
Surname web-pages are listed in the following pages:
- A-Z of Ireland Family Surnames Page
  members.tripod.com/~Caryl_Williams/Eirenames-7.html

- Personal Home Pages
  www.CyndisList.com/personal.htm
  Good starting point, but with American bias.

- Cyndis List: Surname, Family Association & Family Newsletters index
  www.cyndislist.com/surnames.htm
  American bias

- Irish Names: Clans and Family Surname Pages
  www.scotlandsclans.com/irclans.htm
  Directory of family pages

- Irish Surname Pages
  www.geocities.com/Athens/Parthenon/6108/surnames.htm

- Irish Surnames and Irish Descendants Homepages
  www.geocities.com/Heartland/Meadows/4404/pages.html
  Brief gateway

- Links to Irish Names
  www.rootsweb.com/~fianna/surname/name02.html
  Surname webpage directory

- Roots Web Surname List
  rsl.rootsweb.com
  International, but with many Irish names

- Surname Helper Home Page
  surhelp.rootsweb.com
  Gateway

- Registry of Websites at Rootsweb
  www.rootsweb.com/~websites/
  Scroll down; probably the most extensive listing of surname sites; American bias

- Surname Resources at Rootsweb
  resources.rootsweb.com/surnames/

The major on-line surname interests listing for Ireland is:
- Online Irish Names Research Directory
  list.jaunay.com/irlnames
  Includes lists for most counties. These are not included in the list below.

See also:
- Curious Fox: Ireland
  www.curiousfox.com/uk/ireland.lasso

- Genealogical Research Directory
  www.ozemail.com.au/~grdxxx
  Webpage for the major published interests listing, available as a book or CD

- Genuki Surname Lists
  www.genuki.org.uk/indexes/SurnamesLists.html
  Interests

- The Irish Ancestral Research Association: Members Surname Interests
  www.tiara.ie/surnames.htm

- Irish Family Register
  www.irishabroad.com/Genealogy/SurnameInfo/ surnameinformation__search.asp
  Surname interest list

- Irish Surname Pages
  www.rootsweb.com/~irllimer/surnames.htm

- Atlas of Family Names in Ireland
  www.ucc.ie:8080/cocoon/doi/atlas

- The Ulster Genealogical Database
  www.ulstersociety.org/genealogy.htm
  Surname interests

A variety of databases can be searched for surnames at:
- Surname Navigator Ireland
  www.kuijsten.de/navigator/ireland

County and Local Surname Websites
Both interests lists and gateways/links pages to websites are included in the following list.

Antrim
- Co. Antrim Families on the Web
  www.geocities.com/Heartland/Prairie/4592/antlink.html

- Co. Antrim Family Surname & Irish Family Surname Interest List
  irishgenealogy.net/antrimgen.html#SURNAME

- The Antrim County Surname List
  www.ole.net/~maggie/antrim/surnames.htm

Carlow
- Carlow Sons and Daughters
  www.rootsweb.com/~irlcar2/families.htm
  Gateway to family sites

- County Carlow Surname Registry
  www.rootsweb.com/~irlcar2/registry.htm

Clare
- County Clare Surname Roster
  www.connorsgenealogy.net/Clare/claresurnamesAtoD.html
  Interest list

Cork
- Ginni Swanton's Web Site: County Cork Surnames Database
  www.ginnisw.com/Surnames%20Home.htm

Donegal
- County Donegal Surname Researchers
  www.geocities.com/Heartland/Estates/6587/Donresearch.html
  Web pages

Down
- County Down Family Genealogies
  www.rootsweb.com/~nirdow/genealogies.shtml

Galway
- County Galway Surname List
  www.labyrinth.net.au/~quibellg/galway.htm

- Family History Home Pages
  www.rootsweb.com/~irlgal/homepagesam.htm
  For Galway

Kerry
- Family Association Websites
  www.rootsweb.com/~irlker/familywebs.html
  For Co. Kerry

Kilkenny
- Surnames of Co. Kilkenny
  www.rootsweb.com/irlkik/ksurname.htm
  Click on 'Surnames'

- County Kilkenny, Ireland, Genealogy: Surnames of Co. Kilkenny
  www.rootsweb.com/~irlkik/ksurname.htm#sons
  Gateway to surname pages, coats of arms, etc.

Laois
- County Leix/Laois Surnames
  www.rootsweb.com/~irllex/surnames.htm
  Links page to family websites

Leitrim
- County Leitrim Surnames
  www.rootsweb.com/~irlleitr/surnames.htm
  Surname sites link page

- County Leitrim Surnames
  www.rootsweb.com/~irllet/surnames.htm
  Links page to family sites

- Leitrim-Roscommon Surname Search Page
  www.leitrim-roscommon.com/surname__intro.html

Limerick
- County Limerick Surname Roster
  www.connorsgenealogy.com/LIM/
  Click on title

Londonderry
- Derry Surname Registry
  www.rootsweb.com/~nirldy2/surnames__for__derry.htm
  Interests list

- Londonderry Surname Queries
  www.thauvin.net/chance/ireland/derry/queries.jsp

Longford
- Longford Surnames Online
  www.rootsweb.com/~irllog/longford.htm
  Links page

Mayo
- The County Mayo Surname Interest List
  genuki.cs.ncl.ac.uk/SurnamesList/MAY.html

- County Mayo Surnames
  www.rootsweb.com/~irlmayo/surnames.htm
  Links page for surname sites

Meath
- County Meath Surnames, Lineages, Family Histories
  www.rootsweb.com/~irlmea2/Surname/lineages.htm
  Interests list

Roscommon
See Leitrim

Tipperary
- County Tipperary Surname Registry
  www.rootsweb.com/~irltip2/registry.htm
  Interests

- County Tipperary Surnames
  www.rootsweb.com/~irltip/surnames.htm
  In part, a gateway to family webpages

- Tipperary Surnames
  homepages.ihug.co.nz/~hughw/tip.html

- Tipperary Surnames Online
  www.rootsweb.com/~irltip2/surnames.htm
  Links page

Tyrone
- County Tyrone Surname Project
  www.rootsweb.com/~nirtyr/co-tyrone-surname.htm
  Interests list

Waterford
- County Waterford Surname Registry
  www.rootsweb.com/~irlwat2/registry.htm

Westmeath
- County Westmeath Surname Registry
  www.rootsweb.com/~irlwem2/registry.htm
  Interests

Wexford
- The Wexford Surnames List
  homepages.ihug.co.nz/~hughw/wexford.html

9. Births, Marriages and Deaths

Introductions

- Civil Records: Birth, Marriage and Death Registration
  www.from-ireland.net/gene/civilregistration.htm
- Civil Registration
  freepages.genealogy.rootsweb.com/~irishancestors/
  Civil%20registration.html
- Finding Irish Civil Registration Records
  www.allaboutirish.com/library/gen/civreg.shtm
- Ginni Swanton's Web Site: Irish Birth, Death, and Marriage Civil Records
  www.ginnisw.com/irish3.htm
- The General Register Office
  www.groireland.ie
  Includes a page on 'Registering the People: 150 years of civil registration'
- General Register Office Northern Ireland
  www.groni.gov.uk
- A guide to the General Register Office of Ireland
  homepage.eircom.net/~seanjmurphy/gro/
- IGSI: Irish Civil Registration / Kyle J. Betit & Dwight A. Radford
  www.irishgenealogical.org/igsi__published/cens__sub/homabd01.htm
- Ireland: Superintendent Registrars Districts by County
  www.rootsweb.com/~bifhsusa/irishregnc.html
- State Registration of Births Marriages and Deaths
  scripts.ireland.com/ancestor/browse/records/state
- How to Order B/M/D Certificates
  www.rootsweb.com/~irltip2/howto.htm
- How to Order B/M/D
  www.rootsweb.com/~irllex/howto.htm

- Film Numbers for L.D.S. Index to their Irish B.D.M. Films
  www.rootsweb.com/~fianna/guide/lds-bdm.html
  List of microfilms of civil registration indexes 1864-1921
- Irish Birth Films
  www.genfindit.com/ibirths.htm
  Civil registration post 1864 at the Latter Day Saints
- Irish Marriage Films
  www.genfindit.com/imarrs.htm
  Civil registration post 1845 at the Latter Day Saints
- Irish Death Films
  www.genfindit.com/ideaths.htm
  Civil registration post 1864 at the Latter Day Saints
- BMDs by Registration Districts
  www.from-ireland.net/gene/district.htm
  Includes some indexes to civil registers

Parish Registers: Introductory

- Churches and Searches
  www.rootsweb.com/~fianna/county/churches.html
  Searching in church registers
- Church Records
  www.from-ireland.net/gene/churchrcds.htm
  Includes pages for each denomination, with links to county pages
- Parish Registers of the Churches
  freepages.genealogy.rootsweb.com/~irishancestors/
  Parish%20registers.html
- C.M.C.
  www.cmrcp.net
  Christenings, marriages and cemetery records; county pages listed below. Also includes some extracts from other records
- LDS Film Numbers for Ireland Parish Registers
  www.rootsweb.com/~fianna/county/ldspars.html

- Parish Records and Marriage Licence Bonds
  www.nationalarchives.ie/genealogy/church.html
  From the National Archives

- Parish Registers in the National Library of Ireland
  www.nli.ie/pdfs/famil2.pdf
  General discussion

- Church of Ireland Index
  www.proni.gov.uk/records/private/cofiindx.htm
  List of microfilmed parish registers (not indexed by personal name) at
  the Public Record Office of Northern Ireland

- Church of Ireland Parish Records: Earliest Dates
  irelandgenealogyprojects.rootsweb.com/Old__IGW/coirecs.html
  Also includes pages for Presbyterians and Roman Catholics

- Church Records
  www.from-ireland.net/gene/churchrecrds.htm
  Introduction

- Ireland I.G.I. Batch Numbers
  freepages.genealogy.rootsweb.com/~hughwallis/IGIBatchNumbers/
  CountryIreland.htm

- Marriage and Burial Records of Irish Presbyterians
  www.ancestry.com/learn/library/article.aspx?=7473

- Roman Catholic Records
  scripts.ireland.com/ancestor/browse/counties/rcmaps/
  Comprehensive listing of registers for every Irish parish

National Databases

- Ireland: Births or Baptisms, Deaths & Marriages Exchange
  www.thauvin.net/chance/ireland/bmd/

- Irish Church Records: Baptisms and Marriages
  freepages.genealogy.rootsweb.com/~irishchurchrecords/
  Database with entries contributed by users

- Irish Marriages 1771-1812
  www.ancestry.com/search/db.aspx?dbid=6404

- Master Marriage Index
  www.ajmorris.com/roots/mmi/mmi.htm
  Index to marriages of persons with Irish surnames; source indexed not
  stated

- Irish Index
  www.irishindex.ca/
  15,000 birth, marriage and death announcements from *Freeman's
  journal*, 1817-23

- Irish Marriages: being an index to the marriages in *Walker's
  Hibernian Magazine* 1771 to 1812
  www.celticcousins.net/ireland/irish-marriages.htm

- Index to the births marriages and deaths in *Anthologia Hibernica*,
  1793-1794
  www.celticcousins.net/ireland/anthologia__hibernica.htm

County & Local Pages

Antrim

- Birth, Death and Marriage Records for County Antrim and County
  Down
  www.ancestryireland.com/database.php?filename=db__QUIS
  Membership required

- County Antrim Church of Ireland Records
  www.rootsweb.com/~fianna/county/antrim/antcoi.html

- Co. Antrim Church Records
  www.rootsweb.com/~fianna/county/antrim/ant-chur.html

- County Antrim Presbyterian Church Records: Dates and Source
  Locations
  www.rootsweb.com/~fianna/county/antrim/antpres.html

- County Antrim Roman Catholic Parishes
  www.rootsweb.com/~fianna/county/antrim/antrc.html

- Antrim Roman Catholic Records
  scripts.ireland.com/ancestor/browse/counties/rcmaps/antrimrc.htm

- Antrim County: Roman Catholic Parish Records, Ireland: Baptismal and
  Marriage Parish Record Index
  www.from-ireland.net/parishrecords/ant/antrimcindex.htm

Ballymoney
- Ballymoney Anglican Church
  www.4qd.org/bann/church/BallymoneyAng/Marriages.html
  1846-62; incomplete

Belfast
- Search Rosemary Street Church Records, Belfast, Ireland
  www.ancestorsatrest.com/church__records/
  rosemary__street__church__ireland.shtml
  Births 1822-67; marriages 1811-45.

Island Magee
- Island Magee parish marriage records
  www.britishislesgenweb.org/northernireland/antrim/
  islandmagee.html
  19th c. This page has been removed from the web, but an archived copy
  may still be read at **web.archive.org**

Kilrea
- Kilrea First Presbyterian Church Records
  www.4qd.org/bann/church/KilreaFirstPres/index.html
  Baptisms 1825-95; marriages 1825-45. In progress. Also gravestone
  inscriptions, *etc.*

Monkstown
- Burials 1878-1889
  freepages.history.rootsweb.com/~stephenbarnes/monkstown/
  burials.htm

  At Monkstown, Belfast. Continued as follows:
  1890-99 **/burials1.htm**
  1900-1909 **/burials2.htm**
  1910-1919 **/burials3.htm**
  1920-1953 **/burials4.htm**
  Surname index **/surname.htm**

The Vow
- Bann Valley Church Records: The Vow Cemetery
  www.4qd.org/bann/church/Vow/Vow.html

Armagh
- Co. Armagh Church Records
  www.rootsweb.com/~fianna/county/armagh/arm-chur.html

- County Armagh Church of Ireland Records
  www.rootsweb.com/~fianna/county/armagh/armcoi.html

- County Armagh Presbyterian Church Records
  www.rootsweb.com/~fianna/county/armagh/armpres.html

- Armagh County Roman Catholic Parish Records, Ireland
  www.from-ireland.net/parishrecords/arm/armindex.htm

- Co. Armagh Roman Catholic Parishes and Dates
  www.rootsweb.com/~fianna/county/armagh/armrc.html

- Armagh Marriages as posted to the Armagh Mailing List
  www.rootsweb.com/~nirarm2/records/Marriages.htm

Carlow
- County Carlow Church of Ireland Records: earliest dates and source
  locations
  www.rootsweb.com/~fianna/county/carlow/carcoi.html
  List with locations

- County Carlow Roman Catholic Parishes
  www.rootsweb.com/~fianna/county/carlow/carrc.html
  Lists register held by the Latter Day Saints

- County Carlow Roman Catholic Parish Records
  www.from-ireland.net/parishrecords/carlow/carlowrcindex.htm

Ballon
- Roman Catholic Parish Records Indices: Ballon & Ratoe Roman
  Catholic Parish, Co. Carlow, Ireland: Marriage Index 1836 to 1838
  www.from-ireland.net/parishrecords/carlow/ballonmars1836.htm

Carlow
- The Scots Church Records: May 1832-April 1893: Presbyterian Church
  in Carlow Christening
  www.rootsweb.com/~irlcar2/Scots__Church__records.htm

Fenagh
- Catholic Parish Registers of Fenagh and Myshall, Co. Carlow, Ireland, 1822-1880
  familytreemaker.genealogy.com/users/c/L/e/

          Susan-Clement-Swansea/FILE/0025page.html

Myshall
See also Fenagh
- Baptism Records, Myshall Parish, Co. Carlow
  www.rootsweb.com/~irlcar2/fenagh.htm
  Covers 1842-58

Ratoe
See Ballon

Cavan
- Listing of Church of Ireland Baptismal Registers for County Cavan
  freepages.genealogy.rootsweb.com/~adrian/Cav__CIB1.htm

- County Cavan: Church of Ireland: Dates and Source Locations
  www.rootsweb.com/~fianna/county/cavan/cavcoi.html

- Church of Ireland Records
  www.sierratel.com/colinf/genuki/CAV/CofI.htm
  Directory of microfilmed/indexed baptism, marriage and burial registers for Co. Cavan
  For Methodist registers, see **/Methodist.htm**
  For Presbyterian registers, see **/Presby.htm**
  For Quaker registers, see **/Quaker.html**
  For Roman Catholic registers, see **/RC.htm**

- Listing of Church of Ireland Baptismal Registers for County Cavan
  freepages.genealogy.rootsweb.com/~adrian/Cav__CIB1.htm

- County Cavan Presbyterian Church Records: Dates and Source Locations
  www.rootsweb.com/~fianna/county/cavan/cavpres.html

- Cavan County: Roman Catholic Parish Records
  www.from-ireland.net/parishrecords/cavan/cavanrcindex.htm

- County Cavan Roman Catholic Parishes: Dates and Source Locations
  www.rootsweb.com/~fianna/county/cavan/cavrc.html

- Listing of Roman Catholic Baptismal Registers for County Cavan
  freepages.genealogy.rootsweb.com/~adrian/Cav__RCB1.htm

Ashfield
- Ashfield Parish, Co. Cavan Baptismal Register (1821-1864)
  freepages.genealogy.rootsweb.com/~adrian/Ash__Bap1.htm
  See also **/Ash__Bap2.htm**

- Ashfield Parish Area of Co. Cavan. Partial Marriage Register (1845-1917)
  freepages.genealogy.rootsweb.com/~adrian/Ash__Mar1.htm

- Ashfield Parish Area of Co. Cavan Partial Burial Register (1819-1984)
  freepages.genealogy.rootsweb.com/~adrian/Ash__Bur1.htm

Drumgoon
- Drumgoon Parish Area of Co. Cavan. Baptismal Register Extracts (1802-1864)
  freepages.genealogy.rootsweb.com/~adrian/Dgn__Bap2.htm
  Brief

Drung
- L.D.S. Parish Register Printouts. Drung Parish, Co. Cavan. Christenings 1735-1827
  freepages.genealogy.rootsweb.com/~adrian/LDSBap01.htm

Enniskeen See also Kilbride
- Deaths in Roman Catholic Parish of Enniskeen, Kingscourt, County Cavan, Ireland
  www.irelandgenweb.com/~irlcav2/enniskeen-deaths.html
  For Enniskeen, 1846-50

Kilbride
- Parish Register for the Diocese of Meath, Parishes of Kilbride & Mountnugent (Civil Parishes of Enniskeen, Kilbride and Loughan)
  www.rootsweb.com/~irlcav/bride.htm
  For 1832-4, *etc.*

Kingscourt See also Enniskeen
- [Extractions from Immaculate Conception Roman Catholic Church, Kingscourt, 1864-1877]
  www.rootsweb.com/~irlcav/Kingsco.htm
  19th c.

Loughan
See Kilbride

Mountnugent
See Kilbride

Clare

- Parishes and Church Records
  www.clarelibrary.ie/eolas/coclare/genealogy/parishes.htm
  In Co. Clare

- County Clare Church of Ireland Parish Records
  www.rootsweb.com/~fianna/county/clare/clacoi.html

- County Clare Church of Ireland Parish Registers
  home.pacbell.net/nymets11/genuki/CLA/CoIrecordsi.htm

- Baptisms, Marriage and other Records: [Co. Clare]
  www.rootsweb.com/~irlcla/Surname.html

- County Clare Church of Ireland Parish Registers
  home.pacbell.net/nymets11/genuki/CLA/COIrecordsi.htm

- County Clare CMC Record Project
  www.cmcrp.net/Clare/

- Clare County Roman Catholic Parish Records
  www.from-ireland.net/parishrecords/clare/clarercindex.htm

- County Clare Roman Catholic Parish Registers, with earliest recorded date
  home.pacbell.net/nymets11/genuki/CLA/RCrecords.htm

- County Clare Roman Catholic Records
  www.rootsweb.com/~fianna/county/clare/clarc.html

- Assorted Co. Clare Marriages August 1851-June 1862
  www.connorsgenealogy.com/clare/ClareMarriages.htm

Feakle
- Clare County Roman Catholic Parish Records: Feakle
  www.from-ireland.net/parishrecords/clare/feacleind.htm
  Index, 1860-61

Inchicronan
- County Clare, Inchicronan Parish, Sranagalloon: Baptisms 1860-1880
  www.connorsgenealogy.com/clare/Sranagalloon.htm

Killard
- Co. Clare Baptisms: Killard/Kilrush/Kilmurry/Kilmacduane
  freepages.genealogy.rootsweb.com/~msjenkins/records/clarebap.htm

Kilmaley
- Kilmaley Parish Baptism Records, County Clare, Ireland
  www.rootsweb.com/~irlcla/Kilmaley.html
  For 1882-90. Continued for 1891-8 at /Kilmaley2.html and
  for 1899-1900 at /Kilmaley3.html

Kilmihil
- [Kilmihil]
  www.kilmihil.com/history/genealogy/
  Includes baptisms, marriages, and graveyard records

Liscannor
- Deaths in the Liscannor Area 1864-1870
  www.clarelibrary.ie/eolas/coclare/genealogy/
                       deaths__in__the__liscannor__area.htm
  From civil registers

Sranagalloon
See Inchicronan

Cork

- County Cork Civil Registrations
  myhome.ispdr.net.au/~mgrogan/cork/a__civil.htm
  Many pages of indexes to and extracts from civil registration for
  particular places

- County Cork CMC Record Project
  www.cmcrp.net/Cork/index.html
  Christenings, marriages and cemetery records

- County Cork Church of Ireland Records
  www.rootsweb.com/~fianna/county/cork/corcoi.html
  Commencement dates only

- County Cork Roman Catholic Records
  www.rootsweb.com/~fianna/county/cork/corrc.html

Aghada
- Aghada RC Parish Records
  www.geocities.com/Wellesley/Commons/3717/
  Birth and marriage databases

Baillincuslane
See Drishane

Ballyhay
- Ballyhay Christenings 1727-1875, Co. Cork
  myhome.ispdr.net.au/~mgrogan/cork/ballyhay.htm
  Index

Ballymoney
- Ballymoney Parish Records 1805-1873
  www.paulturner.ca/Ireland/Cork/Ballymoney%20Parish/
  BP-text-1.htm

Ballyneen
- Ballyneen District Deaths by surname
  www.ginnisw.com/Ballineen%20District%20Deaths.html
  From the civil registers 1864-70

Ballyvourney
- Ballyvourney Roman Catholic Baptisms 1810-1824, Co. Cork
  myhome.ispdr.net.au/~mgrogan/cork/ballyvourney__bapt.htm

Bandon
- Births registered in Bandon. Co. Cork 1870
  uk.geocities.com/irishancestralpages/bandon1870b.html

Boherbue
See Mallow

Currens
See Currow

Currow
- Baptisms Currow RC Parish (Killeentierna and Currens) Diocese of Kerry, Co. Cork
  myhome.ispdr.net.au/~mgrogan/cork/patty__0823802.htm
  Covers 1801-3

Derinagree
See Dromtariffe

Drishane
- Deaths 1864-1869: Townlands in the Parish of Drishane; Townships in the Parish of Ballincuslane, Co. Cork
  myhome.ispdr.net.au/~mgrogan/cork/patty__0823801.htm

Dromtariffe
- Baptisms 1832 for Dromtariffe and Derinagree RC, Barony of Duhallow, Diocese of Kerry, Co. Cork
  myhome.ispdr.net.au/~mgrogan/cork/dromtariffe__bapt.htm

Dunmanway
- Dunmanway Baptisms and Marriages, St. Patricks, Co. Cork
  myhome.ispdr.net.au/~mgrogan/cork/dunmanway.htm
  Index, 19th c.

Enniskeane
- Catholic Baptisms Enniskeane, Co. Cork
  www.ginnisw.com/Baptisms%20Enniskeane%20RC%20records.htm
  Mid-19th c.

- Catholic Marriages in Enniskeane
  www.ginnisw.com/Enniskeane%20RC%20Marriages.htm
  Covers 1815-1932

- Deaths from Enniskeane Parish Register and Ahiohill Cemetery
  www.ginnisw.com/Deaths%20Enniskeane%20Ahiohill.htm

Inchigeelagh
- Inchigeelach RC Baptisms July-Dec 1863. Inchigeelach Marriages 1816-1817, Co. Cork
  myhome.ispdr.net.au/~mgrogan/cork/inch__pp.htm

- Inchigeelagh Church Records, Co. Cork, from O'Kief, Coshe Mang, Slieve Lougher & Upper Blackwater in Ireland 1816 thru 1900
  myhome.ispdr.net.au/mgrogan/cork/inch__m.htm
  Marriages

Killeentierna
See Currow

Kilmicahel
- RC Parish of Kilmicahel: Marriages 1819-1855; Baptisms 1821-1851. Co. Cork
  myhome.ispdr.net.au/~mgrogan/cork/kilmich__reg.htm

Kilmichael
- Roman Catholic Parish Records, Co. Cork, Ireland: Kilmichael Parish. Baptismal Index, 1847
  www.from-ireland.net/parishrecords/cork/kilmichael1847.baps.htm

Kilmurry
- Kilmurry RC Parish Records: Baptisms June 2 1786 to Feb 1812; Marriages 1803-1805
  myhome.ispdr.net.au/~mgrogan/cork/kilmurry.htm

- Kilmurry Marriages 1826, 1836, 1837, Co. Cork
  myhome.ispdr.net.au/~mgrogan/cork/kilmurry__m.htm

Kinneigh
- Kinneigh Parish Records 1795-1854
  www.paulturner.ca/Ireland/Cork/Kinneigh__Parish/
  kinneigh-parish-text-1.htm

Mallow
- Boherbue, Mallow Baptismal Records 1863, Co. Cork
  myhome.ispdr.net.au/~mgrogan/cork/boherbue.htm

Ovens
- Marriages: Parish of Ovens, Co. Cork
  myhome.ispdr.net.au/mgrogan/cork/ovens.htm
  For 1839-47

Donegal
- County Donegal Church of Ireland Records
  www.rootsweb.com/~fianna/county/donegal/doncoi.html

- County Donegal Presbyterian Church Records
  www.rootsweb.com/~fianna/county/donegal/donpres.html

- County Donegal Roman Catholic Parishes
  www.rootsweb.com/~fianna/county/donegal/donrc.html

- Donegal County Roman Catholic Parish Records, Ireland: Baptismal and Marriage Parish Record Index
  www.from-ireland.net/parishrecords/don/donindex.htm

- Donegal County Roman Catholic Parish Records
  www.from-ireland.net/parishrecords/don/donindex.htm
  List of registers available

Ballintra
- St. Brigid's Roman Catholic Church, Ballintra: Parish Register Extracts: Baptisms 1866-1913; Marriages 1866-1945
  freepages.genealogy.rootsweb.com/~donegal/stbridsballintra.htm

Church Hill
- Church Hill Civil Registrations
  freepages.genealogy.rootsweb.com/~donegal/gartan/chhname.htm
  Index, 1850's & 1860's.

Cloncha
- Cloncha Parish births 1669 to 1783: extracts from the parish registers
  freepages.genealogy.rootsweb.com/~donegal/clonchareg.htm

Clonmany
- Roman Catholic Marriages for the parish of Clonmany (1852-1900)
  www.iol.ie/~inishowen/genealogy/records/Clonmany/Marriage/
  index.html

Crossroads
- Crossroads Presbyterian Church, County Donegal, Ireland: Church Records
  mcn.ie/crossroads/genealogy/intro.html
  Births from 1811, deaths 1854-95, marriages, 19-20th c.

Donaghmore

- Derry Roman Catholic Diocese Donaghmore Parish: Marriages
  www.from-ireland.net/diocs/donaghmore5767.htm
  1860's & 1870's. Also baptisms 1840-45.

Glenties

- St. Connell's, Glenties, Baptisms, Oct. 1866-Jan 1870.
  freepages.genealogy.rootsweb.com/~donegal/fintownreg.htm

Kilteevoge

- Kilteevoge Marriages 1855-1880
  freepages.genealogy.rootsweb.com/~donegal/kilteevogemarr.htm

Laghey

- [Laghey]
  www.sadelson.com/Genealogy/Laghey_Parish.htm
  Includes 18th c. baptisms and marriages. In progress.

Raphoe

- Union of Strabane Death Index ... Deaths Registered in the District of
  Raphoe
  freepages.genealogy.rootsweb.com/~donegaleire/Raphdeath.html
  For 1866-7

Down

See also Antrim
- County Down Church of Ireland Parish Records
  www.rootsweb.com/~fianna/county/down/dowcoi.html

- County Down Church of Ireland Parish Records
  www.rootsweb.com/~nirdow2/Old_Down/COI_Parish.htm

- County Down Presbyterian Records
  www.rootsweb.com/~nirdow2/Old_Down/Presbyterian.htm

- County Down Presbyterian Records
  www.rootsweb.com/~fianna/county/down/dowpres.html

- County Down Roman Catholic Records
  www.rootsweb.com/~fianna/county/down/dowrc.html

- County Down Burial Index 1700s
  www.rootsweb.com/~nirdow2/Burial/down_index.htm

- County Down Marriage Record Resources
  www.rootsweb.com/~nirdow/marriages/marriages.shtml
  Index of contributed entries

Banbridge

- Marriage Register of the Presbyterian Congregation of Banbridge,
  County Down, 1756-1794
  freepages.genealogy.rootsweb.com/~donaghmore1/banmarreg.html
  www.raymondscountydownwebsite.com/html/banbridge_a.html

- Banbridge Area, Co. Down Marriages: some Presbyterian Marriages
  1848-1864
  freepages.genealogy.rootsweb.com/~donaghmore1/bannprmar.html

Clonallen

- Roman Catholic Parish Records, Co. Down, Northern Ireland: Clonallen
  (Warrenpoint) Roman Catholic Parish, Diocese of Dromore: Marriage
  Index 1826-1828
  www.from-ireland.net/parishrecords/down/clonnallenmarrs26.htm

Donaghmore

- Donaghmore Register of Baptisms 1804-1900
  freepages.genealogy.rootsweb.com/~donaghmore1/donaghmore/
  donvrbapt1.html

- Donaghmore Marriages 1846-1900
  freepages.genealogy.rootsweb.com/~donaghmore1/donaghmore/
  donvrmar1.html

- Glascar Presbyterian Church Records, Glaskermore, Donaghmore Parish
  freepages.genealogy.rootsweb.com/~donaghmore1/donaghmor/
  glascarprch.html

  1781-1832

Glaskermore

See Donaghmore

Inch

- Search Inch Parish Records 1788-1872, Ireland
  www.ancestorsatrest.com/church_records/
  inch_parish_records_burials.shtml
  Burials only, to 1841 at present

Kilgeever
- Kilgeever Parish Marriage Records
  freepages.genealogy.rootsweb.com/%7Edeesegenes/kmar.htm
  1844-45, etc.

Kilkeel
- Kilkeel Roman Catholic Parish Records: Baptismal Extracts, County
  Down, Ulster, Ireland
  www.from-ireland.net/parishrecords/down/kilkeelrc456061.htm
  For 1845 & 1860-62

- Kilkeel Parish Marriages
  www.raymondscountydownwebsite.com/html/
  kilkeel,marraiges%20and%20births.htm
  19th c., also births

Lower Drumgooland
- Roman Catholic Parish Records: Lower Drumgooland Roman Catholic
  Parish, Diocese of Dromore
  www.from-ireland.net/parishrecords/down/
  drumgoolandLr1832baps.htm

Newry
- Partial Newry Marriage & Baptism Records from L.D.S. Microfilm
  freepages.genealogy.rootsweb.com/%7Edonaghmore1/
  newrymarbap.html

  For 1784-1820

Warrenpoint
See Clonallen

Dublin
- County Dublin: Church of Ireland Records
  www.rootsweb.com/~fianna/county/dublin/dubcoi.html
  List with locations

- County Dublin Roman Catholic Records
  www.rootsweb.com/~fianna/county/dublin/dubrc.html

- County Dublin C.M.C. Record Project
  cmcrp.net/Dublin/index.html
  i.e. christenings, marriages, and cemetery records. Contributed entries.

- Dublin Heritage
  www.dublinheritage.ie
  Database of births, marriages and burials for Dublin

Baldoyle
- Baldoyle, Howth & Kinsealy Roman Catholic Parish. Some Baptismal
  Extracts 1784-88 & notes on condition of Register/Film
  www.from-ireland.net/parishrecords/dub/baldoyle1784.htm

Dublin
- The Register of the Parish of S. Peter and S. Kevin, Dublin
  content.ancestry.com/iexec/?htx=BookList&dbid=28938

Howth
See Baldoyle

Kinsealy
See Baldoyle

Monkstown
- Search Extracts from the Parochial Returns of the Parish of
  Monkstown, Dublin
  www.ancestorsatrest.com/church__records/
  parochia__returns__parish__monkstown.shtml
  Burials 1783-1800

Fermanagh
- County Fermanagh Roman Catholic Records
  www.rootsweb.com/~fianna/county/fermanagh/ferrc.html
  Mostly held by the Latter Day Saints

- County Fermanagh Roman Catholic Parish Records
  www.genuki.org.uk/big/irl/FER/RCRecords.html

Aghalurcher
- Aghalurcher Parish
  www.rootsweb.com/~nirfer/aghalurcher__parish.html
  Includes baptisms, marriages and burials 1804-15

Aghavea
- Aghavea Parish
  www.rootsweb.com/~nirfer/aghavea__parish.htm
  Includes index to marriages, mid-19th c.

Belleek
- These are a few marriages from Belleek Parish
www.rootsweb.com/~nirfer/belleek__mar.htm
Index, late 19th c.

Cleenish
- These are a few marriages from Cleenish Parish
www.rootsweb.com/~nirfer/cleenish__mar.htm

Clones
- These are a few Marriages from Clones Parish
www.rootsweb.com/~nirfer/clones__mar.htm
Index, mid-19th c.

Derryvullan
- These are a few Marriages from Derryvullan Parish
www.rootsweb.com/~nirfer/derryvullan__mar.htm
Index, 1860's & 1870's.

Devenish
- Parish of Devenish, County Fermanagh, Burials
www.rootsweb.com/~nirfer2/Documents/Cemeteries/
Devenish__Graveyard.doc

  19th c.

- Some Marriages from Devenish Parish
www.rootsweb.com/~nirfer/devenish__mar1.htm
Index, mid-19th c.

Drumkeeran
- Some Marriages from Drumkeeran Parish
www.rootsweb.com/~nirfer/drumkeeran1.htm
Index, mid-19th c.

Enniskillen
- Enniskillen Parish
www.rootsweb.com/~nirfer/enniskillen.html
Baptisms, marriages and burials, 17-19th c., etc.

Galloon
- These are a few marriages from Galloon Parish
www.rootsweb.com/~nirfer/galloon__mar.htm
Index, c.1850-75

Inishmacsaint
- Inishmacsaint Parish
www.rootsweb.com/~nirfer/inishmar.html
Includes baptisms, marriages and burials, 19th c.

Killesher
- Some Marriages from Killesher Parish
www.rootsweb.com/~nirfer/Killesher__mar.htm
Index

Kinawley
- These are a few marriages from Kinawley Parish
www.rootsweb.com/~nirfer/Kinawley__mar.htm
Index, 1850's-70's

Lisnaskea
- Index to Register of Baptisms, Marriages, Burials & Publications of
Banns in the Parish of Lisnaskea in the County of Fermanagh and
Diocese of Clogher
www.ulsterancestry.com/BDM__Clogher.html
Early 19th c.

- Some Marriages from the Lisnaskea Area
www.rootsweb.com/~nirfer/lisnaskea__mar.htm
Index, 1850's-70's

Magheracross
- These are a few marriages from Magheracross Parish
www.rootsweb.com/~nirfer/magheracross__mar.htm
Index, 1850's & 1860's

Magheraculmoney
- These are a few Marriages from Magheraculmoney Parish
www.rootsweb.com/nirfer/magheraculmoney__mar.htm
Index, 1860's & 1870's

Rossory
- Some Marriages from Rossory Parish
  www.rootsweb.com/~nirfer/rossory__mar.htm
  Index, mid-19th c.

Tullynageeran
- Tullynageeran GYD, from the *Clogher record* of 1959
  www.rootsweb.com/~nirfer2/Documents/Cemeteries/
  Tullynageeran__Graveyard.doc

Trory
- Some Marriages from Trory Parish
  www.rootsweb.com/~nirfer/trory__mar.htm
  Index, mid-19th c.

Galway
- County Galway Roman Catholic Records
  www.rootsweb.com/~fianna/county/galway/galrc.html
  Held by the Latter Day Saints

- Galway County: Roman Catholic Parish Records
  www.from-ireland.net/parishrecords/gal/galwayrcindex.htm

- Baptism Records Galway
  www.rootsweb.com/~irlgal/baptism__records.htm
  Various brief extracts from parish registers

- Marriage Records, Galway
  www.rootsweb.com/~irlgal/marriage__records.htm
  Various brief extracts from parish registers

- Death Records, Galway
  www.rootsweb.com/~irlgal/death__records.htm
  Various brief extracts from civil registers

Ahascragh
- Diocese of Elphin, Co. Galway: Marriages and Baptisms
  www.rootsweb.com/%7Eirlgal/index6.htm
  Extracts, mainly from Ahascragh and Killosolon

Ardrahan
- Galway County Roman Catholic Records Ardrahan
  www.from-ireland.net/parishrecords/gal/ardrahanextracts.htm
  19th c. extracts

Beagh
- Beagh Parish, Galway Baptisms
  www.celticcousins.net/ireland/beaghbaptisms.htm
  Covers 1850-51, 1855-7

- Beagh Parish, Galway: Baptisms 1860-61
  www.celticcousins.net/ireland/beaghbaptisms60to61.htm
  Continued for 1862 at /beaghbaptisms1862.htm

- Beagh Parish, Galway, Marriages
  www.celticcousins.net/ireland/beaghmarriages.htm
  Roman Catholic, 1860-63

Cummer
- Tuam Diocese: Cummer Parish
  pw2.netcom.com/~lgbl/tuamcumm.html
  Marriages 1813-16

- Marriages of Parish Cummer, Diocese Tuam
  www.rootsweb.com/~irlcnn/Tuam/Marriages/Marriages.htm
  For 1813-16 at present

Killaronan
See Killian

Killosolon
See Ahascragh

Killeenadeem
- Killeenadeem and Kilteskill, May 1, 1836 through December 12, 1880
  www.rootsweb.com/~irlgal/index30.htm

- Diocese of Clonfert, Parish of Killeenadeema, Baptisms
  www.rootsweb.com/~irlgal/index12.htm
  Extracts only, 1837-66

Kilteskill
See Killeenadeema

Killian
- Diocese of Elphin, Parish of Killian and Killaronan Baptisms
  May 17, 1860-November 21 1880
  www.rootsweb.com/~irlgal/index26.htm
  For 1860-67. Continued as follows:
  1868-73 /index.27.htm   1874-80 /index.28.htm

Kiltulla

- County Galway, Diocese of Clonfert. Parish of Kiltulla. Townlands of Gloves, Lower Gloves, Elphin Gloves: Deaths, Baptisms and Marriages
  www.rootsweb.com/~irlgal/index16.htm
  Extracts, c.1828-53

- Co. Galway, Diocese of Clonfert, Parish of Kiltulla (Townland of Gloves): Baptisms June 25, 1844-January 15, 1854
  www.rootsweb.com/~irlgal/index15.htm

- Marriages: Parish Register Catholic Chapelry of Roundstone, Parish of Moyrus, Galway 1888-1889
  www.rootsweb.com/%7Eirlgal/index10.htm

Killosolon
See Ahascragh

Kiltivan
See Roscommon

Loughrea

- Loughrea Cathedral Baptisms 1852
  www.celticcousins.net/ireland/loughrea.htm

- Deaths registered in the District of Loughrea in the Union of Loughrea in the County of Galway
  www.rootsweb.com/~irlgal/index9.htm
  For 1867

Moyrus

- Marriages - Parish Register, Catholic Chapelry of Roundstone, parish of Moyrus, Galway 1888-1889
  www.rootsweb.com/~irlgal/index10.htm

Mullagh

- Roman Catholic Parish Records, Co. Galway, Ireland: Mullagh or Abbeygormican & Killoran (Abbeygormican civil parish) Baptisms 1859-67 (complete)
  www.from-ireland.et/parishrecords/gal/mullagh.htm

Roscommon

- Diocese of Elphin, Co. Galway: Marriages and Baptisms: Parish of Roscommon and Kiltivan
  www.rootsweb.com/~irlgal/index6.htm
  19th c. extracts

Kerry

- Registration Districts in County Kerry
  homepage.eircom.net/~dinglemaps/genuki/KER/Regdists.html

- County Kerry CMC Record Projet
  www.cmcrp.net/Kerry/index.html

- Family History Center Library Catalog Parish Register Film Numbers for County Kerry
  www.rootsweb.com/~irlker/parfilm.html

- On-Line Searchable Database
  www.rootsweb.com/~irlker/addrecords.html
  For Co. Kerry baptisms and marriages

- County Kerry Church of Ireland Records
  www.rootsweb.com/~fianna/county/kerry/kercoi.html

- County Kerry Roman Catholic Records
  www.rootsweb.com/~fianna/county/kerry/kerrc.html

- Baptisms/Birth Records
  www.rootsweb.com/~irlker/birth.html
  Contributed records for Co. Kerry

- Marriage Records, County Kerry, Ireland
  www.rootsweb.com/~irlker/marriage.html
  Contributed records

- Burial/Death Records
  www.rootsweb.com/~irlker/death.html
  Contributed records for Co. Kerry

Annascall

- Birth Records: Civil Registration for the District of Annascall 1864, 1865, 1873 & 1975
  www.rootsweb.com/~irlker/birthannasc6475.html

- Annascall Marriages: Civil Registration: Annascall Registrar's District 1864-1870
  www.rootsweb.com/~irlker/marannal.html

Ballybunion
- Selected Births, Ballybunion
  www.rootsweb.com/~irlker/birthbal.html
  Mid-19th c.

- Burials in Ballybunion, Killehenny Cemetery
  www.rootsweb.com/~irlker/burbalkhen.html
  Index to burial register, 1911-47

Ballyferriter
- Ballyferriter Church Records
  www.geocities.com/Athens/Ithaca/7974/Ballyferriter/church/
  Includes contributed records

Castlegregory
- Civil Registration of Marriages, Castlegregory Registrar's District, Dingle P.L.U. 1864-1870
  www.rootsweb.com/~irlker/marcast1.html

- Castlegregory Deaths: Civil Registration Castlegregory District: Killiney, Cloghane, Stradbally, Ballyduff Civil Parishes, 1864-1870
  www.rootsweb.com/~irlker/deathcast1.htm

Castle Island
- Baptism Locations in Castleisland Roman Catholic Parish
  www.rootsweb.com/~irlker/casparc.html

Currow
- Baptisms 1801-1805, Currow, Co. Kerry
  myhome.ispdr.net.au/~mgrogan/cork/currow/currow__b.htm

Dingle
- Dingle Marriages: Civil Registration: Dingle Registrar's District 1864-1870
  www.rootsweb.com/~irlker/mardingle1.html

- Civil Registration of Marriage: Castlegregory Registrars District: Dingle P.L.U, 1864-1870
  www.rootsweb.com/~irlker/marcast1.html

Keel
- Catholic Parish of Keel and Kiltallagh, Co. Kerry: Marriage Records 1804-1820
  www.myirishancestry.com/index.php/plain/articles/kerry
  Click on title

Killorglin
- Civil Registration Birth Records: Registrar's District of Killorglin
  www.rootsweb.com/~irlker/birthkillorg.html
  For 1866, 1872 & 1875

Kiltallagh
See Keel

Lisselton
- Deaths, Lisselton Area
  www.geocities.com/dalyskennelly__2000/deathslisselton.html
  Late 20th c

Listowel
- Birth Records: Civil Registration for the District of Listowel, 1875-1877
  www.rootsweb.com/~irlker/birthlistow.html

St. Ann's
- Baptism Records, 1830-1833, St. Ann's Parish
  www.rootsweb.com/~irlker/birthard.html

Tralee
- Baptism Records: Tralee
  www.rootsweb.com/~irlker/birthtral.html
  Newspaper birth notices, 1771-97 & 1807-11

Trughanacmy
- Kerry Marriages: an extract of Kerry Marriages for the Barony of Trughanacmy
  familytreemaker.genealogy.com/users/o/r/oPhilip-J-Orourke
  Scroll down for separate pages for 1875, 1876, 1877 & 1887-8
  Also at **www.geocities.com/irishancestralpages/KMmain.html**

Kildare

- County Kildare Roman Catholic Records
  www.rootsweb.com/~fianna/county/kildare/kidrc.html
  Mostly held by the Latter Day Saints

Ardkell

- Baptisms 1899-1916 for the Townland of Ardkell
  pw2.netcom.com/~lgb1/Ardkell.html

Maynooth

- Maynooth, County Kildate, Ireland: Roman Catholic Diocese of Dublin:
  Partial Roman Catholic Baptismal Register Index 1857-1860
  www.from-ireland.net/parishrecords/kild/maynoothb57.htm

Kilkenny

- County Kilkenny, Ireland, Civil Parish Records
  www.rootsweb.com/~irlkik/careclds.htm
  Includes Latter Day Saints film numbers

- County Kilkenny Roman Catholic Records
  www.rootsweb.com/~fianna/county/kilkenny/kilkrc.html
  Mostly held by the Latter Day Saints

- Kilkenny County: Roman Catholic Parish Records
  www.from-ireland.net/parishrecords/kilk/kilkrcindex.htm

- County Kilkenny Catholic Parish Records
  www.rootsweb.com/~irlkik/carerecord.htm
  List of parishes, with earliest dates of registers

Kilkenny

- St. John's (Maldin Street), Kilkenny
  www.rootsweb.com/~fianna/county/kilkenny/kik-mar3.html
  Baptisms 1789-1841; Marriages 1790-1875

- St. Mary's, Kilkenny
  www.rootsweb.com/~fianna/county/kilkenny/kik-mar2.html#bap
  Baptisms 1772-1887; marriages 1755-1858.

- St. Patrick's, Kilkenny Marriages 1800's
  www.rootsweb.com/~fianna/county/kilkenny/kik-mar1.html

Kilmacow

- Kilmacow Parish Birth Index, County Kilkenny, Ireland
  (1858 to 1880)
  www.rootsweb.com/~irlkik/records/kilmindx.htm

Laois

- County Laois Roman Catholic Records
  www.rootsweb.com/~fianna/county/laois/lexrc.html
  Mostly held by the Latter Day Saints

- County Laois Baptismal & Birth Records
  www.rootsweb.com/~irllex/lexbapt.htm
  Index of submitted entries

- County Laois Marriage Records
  www.rootsweb.com/~irllex/lexmar.htm
  Index of submitted entries

Aghaboe

- County Leix Baptism Records: Aghaboe RC Parish, pre 1796-Dec 1999
  www.connorsgenealogy.net/Leix/AghaboeBaptisms.htm
  Index

Grague

- Grague or Graigue Roman Catholic Parish Records: Marriage Extracts,
  Laois (Queens/Leix), Ireland
  www.from-ireland.net/parishrecords/laois/grague1870.htm
  1865-78

Leitrim

- County Leitrim Roman Catholic Records
  www.rootsweb.com/~fianna/county/leitrim/letrc.htm
  Held by the Latter Day Saints

Limerick

- County Limerick Civil Parishes
  www.connorsgenealogy.net/LIM/Parishes.html
  List with notes on registers

- County Limerick CMC Record Project
  www.cmcrp.net/Limerick/Index.html

- Civil Parishes of County Limerick: Available Church Records
  home.pacbell.net/nymets11/genuki/LIM/Parishes.html
  List of parish registers

- County Limerick Roman Catholic Records
  www.rootsweb.com/~fianna/county/limerick/limrc.html
  Commencement dates only

- Limerick County: Roman Catholic Parish Records
  www.from-ireland.net/parishrecords/lim/limrcindex.htm

Londonderry

- Genealogy Records Index
  www.rootsweb.com/~nirldy2/Records/church/churchindex.htm
  Incldes lists of Church of Ireland, Roman Catholic, and Presbyterian
  registers for Londonderry

- Church Records of Derry: Church of Ireland
  www.rootsweb.com/~nirldy/derrycoi.html

- County Derry (Londonderry) Church of Ireland Parish Records
  www.rootsweb.com/~fianna/county/derry/ldycoi.html

- Church Records of Derry: Presbyterian
  www.rootsweb.com/~nirldy/derrypres.html

- County Derry (Londonderry) Presbyterian Records
  www.rootsweb.com/~fianna/county/derry/ldypres.html

- County Derry (Londonderry) Presbyterian Records
  www.rootsweb.com/~nirldy2/Old__Derry/Presbyterian.htm

- Church Records of Derry: Roman Catholic Churches
  www.rootsweb.com/~nirldy/derryrc.html

- County Derry (Londonderry) Roman Catholic Parish Records
  www.rootsweb.com/~fianna/county/derry/ldyrc.html

- Derry Roman Catholic Parish Records
  vicki.thauvin.net/chance/ireland/derry/rcparish.jsp
  www.thauvin.net/chance/ireland/derry/rcparish.jsp
  At the Family History Library

- Ireland Roman Catholic Parish Records: Derry County
  www.rootsweb.com/~nirldy2/Old__Derry/derryrc.htm
  Dates of commencement only

- Londonderry County: Roman Catholic Parish Records, Ireland
  www.from-ireland.net/parishrecords/derry/derryrcindex.htm

Aghadowey

- Aghadowey Church of Ireland
  www.4qd.org/bann/church/AghadoweyCOI/MarriagesBook1.html
  1845-85

- Aghadowey Presbyterian Church Records
  www.4qd.org/bann/church/AghadoweyPresby/index.html
  Marriages 1845-63; also graveyard records

Bovedy

- Bovedy Presbyterian Church Graveyard records
  www.4qd.org/bann/church/Bovedy/Graves.html
  Continued at /Graves2.html

Churchtown

See Tamlaght

Clonmany

- Roman Catholic Marriages for the Parish of Clonmany (1852-1900)
  www.iol.ie/~inishowen/genealogy/records/Clonmany/Marriage/
  index.html
  Index

Garvagh

- Garvagh First Presbyterian Church Records
  www.4qd.org/bann/church/GarvaghFirstPresby/index.html
  Baptisms 1795-1924; marriages 1795-1889. Also graveyard inscriptions

- St. Pauls Church, Garvagh: Records
  www.4qd.org/bann/church/GarvaghStPaul/index.html
  Marriages 1845-89; also graveyard records

Kilrea
- Kilrea Parish Church Records
  www.4qd.org/bann/church/KilreaCOI/index.html
  Some baptisms, marriages and burials, 19th c. Also gravestone inscriptions
- Kilrea Second Presbyterian Church Records
  www.4qd.org/bann/church/KilreaSecPres/index.html
  Baptisms (extracts) 1843-77; marriages (extracts) 1852-1920. Also gravestone inscriptions, *etc.*

Moneydig
- Moneydig Presbyterian Church Records
  www.4qd.org/bann/church/moneydig/index.html
  Baptisms 1857-1923; marriages 1845-1928. Also gravestone inscriptions etc.

Tamlaght
- Bann Valley Church Records: Churchtown Presbyterian Church, Tamlaght
  www.4qd.org/bann/church/Churchtown/index.html
  Baptisms 1840-66; also graveyard inscriptions

Longford
- Church Records
  www.rootsweb.com/~irllog/churchrecs.htm
  Indexes of various registers
- County Longford Church of Ireland Church Registers
  www.rootsweb.com/~irllog/coi__parishes.htm
  List
- County Longford Roman Catholic Parish Records
  personal.nbnet.nb.ca/tmoffatt/RCfilmsLDS.html
  List of LDS films available
- Church Records
  www.rootsweb.com/~irllog/churchrecs.htm
  Includes Killoe marriages, 1826-1917, baptisms 1826-1917, and deaths 1826-84; Clonbroney marriages 1828-99, marriages 1828-99 and deaths, 1828-92; Granard marriages 1778-1894, baptisms 1811-65 and deaths 1811-65; Ardagh & Moydow marriages 1792-1895, baptisms 1793-1895 and deaths 1822-95; Kilcommock marriages 1859-80, baptisms 1859-80, and deaths 1859-80.

- County Longford Baptismal & Birth Records
  www.rootsweb.com/~irllog/longbapt.htm
  Index to submitted entries
- County Longford Marriage Records
  www.rootsweb.com/~irllog/longmar.htm
  Submitted entries

Newtownforbes
- Some Newtownforbes Baptisms
  www.rootsweb.com/~irllog/newtownforbes__bap.htm
  Covers 1829-41

Louth
Church Records in Louth, Ireland
www.rootsweb.com/~irllou/Church

- County Louth Roman Catholic Records
  www.rootsweb.com/~fianna/county/louth/lourc.html
- County Louth Death Notices 1930-1940
  www.jbhall.freeservers.com/death__notices__1930-1940.htm
  From newspapers

Collon
- Collon-Dundalk Church Burials
  www.jbhall.freeservers.com/Collon%20-%20Louth%20Burials.htm
  Collon parish burials 1791-1823; Dundalk, 1790-1802

Dundalk
See Collon

Haggardstown
- Haggardstown Roman Catholic Parish
  www.jbhall.freeservers.com/haggardstown__rc__parish.htm
  Burials from the *Dundalk democrat,* 1868-1900.

Mayo
- County Mayo CMC Record Project
  www.cmcrp.net/Mayo/index.html

- County Mayo Roman Catholic Records
  www.rootsweb.com/~fianna/county/mayo/mayrc.html
  Held by the Latter Day Saints
- County Mayo Roman Catholic Church Records
  www.geocities.com/Heartland/Acres/4031/RCPARISH.HTML
  List of LDS films
- Mayo County Roman Catholic Parish Records
  www.from-ireland.net/parishrecords/mayo/mayocindex.htm
- Births and Baptisms in Parishes Westport - Castlebar, Co. Mayo
  & area
  freepages.genealogy.rootsweb.com/~deesegenes/birth.html
  Extensive; covers many parishes, as do the following:
- Early Marriages in Westport, Newport, Aughagower, Kilgeever,
  Burriscarra, Mayo, Drum, Balla, Co. Mayo, Ireland
  freepages.genealogy.rootsweb.com/~deesegenes/early.htm
- Marriages in Parishes of Castlebar - Westport - Louisburgh,
  Ballintober-Achill, Co. Mayo area
  freepages.genealogy.rootsweb.com/~deesegenes/marr.html

Aglish
See Castlebar

Ardkell
See Roundfort

Aughagower
- Marriages Aughagower Parish 1854 to 1859
  freepages.genealogy.rootsweb.com/~deesegenes/aug.htm
  For 1860-79, see **/maraugh.htm**

Ballintober
- Ballintober Parish Marriages
  freepages.genealogy.rootsweb.com/~deesegenes/tomar1.htm
  1839-49. Continued as follows: 1850-59**/tomar3.htm**
  1860-96 **/tomar2.htm**

Ballysakerry
- Ballysakerry RC Parish Baptisms, Marriages and Deaths 1845-96
  www.connorsgenealogy.net/Mayo/BallysakerryMale-A.htm
  Continued on 5 further pages. Also indexed by females at
  /BallysakerryFemale-A.htm and 5 further pages.

Bohola
- Bohola Parish Baptisms
  www.rootsweb.com/~irlmayo/records/boholabaptisms-A.htm
  Index for 1857-1901. Continued on 13 further pages.

- Bohola Marriages: Husbands
  www.rootsweb.com/~irlmayo/records/boholahusbands-A.htm
  Index 1857-1901. Completed at **/boholahusbands-L.htm**. Also index
  by wives at **/boholawives-A.htm** & **/boholawives-K.htm**

Castlebar
- Castlebar Parish Marriages 1824 to 1839
  freepages.genealogy.rootsweb.com/~deesegenes/cbar.htm

- Marriages in the Castlebar/Aglish Parish, 1840-1855
  freepages.genealogy.rootsweb.com/~deesegenes/agl.htm
  Continued for 1856-82 at **/castle.htm**

Clare Island
- Clare Island Births and Baptisms 1851 to 1872
  freepages.genealogy.rootsweb.com/~deesegenes/clare.htm

Claremorris
- Mayo Abbey Baptisms, Claremorris
  freepages.genealogy.rootsweb.com/~deesegenes/mayoabbey.htm
  1841-3

Crossmolina
- Church of Ireland: Parish Church of Crossmolina
  www.celticcousins.net/ireland/mayocm.htm
  Baptisms 1768-1803

Glanduff
- Baptisms: Glanduff, Co. Mayo, 1872-1879
  www.geocities.com/Heartland/Acres/4031/Glanduff.html

Kilfian

- Kilfian Parish Killala Deaths
  freepages.genealogy.rootsweb.com/~deesegenes/kildeath.html

Kilmoremoy

- [Baptisms for Kilmoremoy Parish, 1823-1830, 1855, 1866]
  www.rootsweb.com/~irlmayo/records/KilmoremoyBaptisms.htm

Kiltimagh

- Kiltimagh, Co. Mayo church records: Baptisms July 1861 to September 1880
  www.rootsweb.com/~fianna/county/mayo/kiltimaghb.html

- Kiltimagh, Co. Mayo, Roman Catholic Marriages
  www.rootsweb.com/~fianna/county/mayo/maymar2.html

Lahardane

- Lahardane Parish Marriages
  freepages.genealogy.rootsweb.com/~deesegenes/lahma.htm
  1842-62

Louisburgh

- County Mayo: Louisburgh Baptisms
  www.connorsgenealogy.net/Mayo/LouisburghBaptisms.htm
  Index, 1850-54. Formerly Kilgeever

Newport

- Newport Births 1879 to 1884
  freepages.genealogy.rootsweb.com/~deesegenes/port.htm

Roundfort

- Roundfort Parish, Co. Mayo: Baptisms 1899-1916 for the Townland of Ardkell
  pw2.netcom.com/~lgbl/Ardkell.html
  Baptisms 1899-1916

Turlough

- County Mayo Civil & Church Records: Turlough Civil Parish: Castlebar Poor Law Union, Carra Barony
  www.connorsgenealogy.net/Mayo/TurloughRecords.htm
  Index to baptisms and marriages, 1847-1911.

Westport

- Westport Parish Marriages 1823 to 1903
  freepages.genealogy.rootsweb.com/~deesegenes/wpt.htm

Meath

County Meath Roman Catholic Records
www.rootsweb.com/~fianna/county/meath/mearc.html
Mostly held by the Latter Day Saints

- Early Marriages for Meath 1776-1829
  ancestorsatrest.com/ireland__genealogy__data/
  meath__marriages.html
  Strays from the parish register of Portpatrick, Wigtownshire, Scotland

Monaghan

- Church Registers for County Monaghan
  ahd.exis.net/monaghan/churchregisters.htm
  www.exis.net/ahd/monaghan/churchregisters.htm

- County Monaghan Church of Ireland Records
  www.rootsweb.com/~fianna/county/monaghan/mogcoi.html

- County Monaghan Presbyterian Records
  www.rootsweb.com/~fianna/county/monaghan/mogpres.html

- County Monaghan Roman Catholic Records
  www.rootsweb.com/~fianna/county/monaghan/mogrc.html

- County Monaghan Roman Catholic Records available in the Mormons FHC
  www.exis.net/ahd/monaghan/fhc-rc.htm

Offaly

- County Offaly Church of Ireland Records
  www.rootsweb.com/~fianna/county/offaly/offcoi.html
  List; also includes Methodists and Quakers

- County Offaly Roman Catholic Records
  www.rootsweb.com/~fianna/county/offaly/offrc.html

Roscommon

- Roscommon: Irish Parish Registers
  www.rootsweb.com/~irlros/irish__parish__registers.htm
  List

- County Roscommon Church of Ireland Records
  www.rootsweb.com/~fianna/county/roscommon/roscoi.html
  List of registers

- County Roscommon Roman Catholic Records
  www.rootsweb.com/~fianna/county/roscommon/rosrc1.html
  List

- County Roscommon Roman Catholic Records
  www.rootsweb.com/~fianna/county/roscommon/rosrc.html
  Held by the Latter Day Saints

- Roscommon County Roman Catholic Parish Records
  www.from-ireland.net/parishrecords/ros/rosscparindex.htm

Athlone
- Athlone Civil Registration District or Poor Law Union, Ireland: Marriage Register Indices
  www.from-ireland.net/xtrs/a/athlonemarrs1.htm
  Also indices to births and deaths, *etc.*

Ballinasloe
- Ballinasloe Civil Registration District or Poor Law Union, Ireland: Marriage Register Indices
  www.from-ireland.net/extrs/b/ballinasloemarrs1.htm
  Also indexes to births and deaths

Roscommon
- Deaths from the Roscommon Town workhouse
  www.geocities.com/Heartland/Pines/7030/page2.html
  List for mid-late 19th c.

Sligo
- County Sligo Church of Ireland and Methodist Records
  www.rootsweb.com/~fianna/county/sligo/slicoi.html
  List

- County Sligo Roman Catholic Parish Registers
  www.rootsweb.com/~irlsli/parish1.html

- County Sligo Roman Catholic Records
  www.rootsweb.com/~fianna/county/sligo/slire.html

- Sligo County Roman Catholic Parish Records
  www.from-ireland.net/parishrecords/sli/sligorcindex.htm

- Extracts of Sligo County
  www.rootsweb.com/~irlsli/microficheopeningshe.html
  From the I.G.I.

Castleconnor
- Castleconnor Parish Records
  www.rootsweb.com/~irlsli/castelconnoropen.html

Kilglass
- Kilglass Parish Births Register
  www.puregolduk.com/bren/kilglass_co_sligo3.htm
  Index, 19th c.

- Kilglass Marriages prior to 1850
  www.puregolduk.com/bren/kilglass_co_sligo4.htm
  Index

- Some Death Records of Kilglass Parish from March 1825 to June 1867
  www.puregolduk.com/bren/kilglass_co_sligo9.htm

Skreen
- Skreen and Dromard Parish Births Register, County Sligo
  www.puregolduk.com/bren/kilglass_co_sligo7.htm
  Click on title

Tipperary
- County Tipperary CMC Record Project
  www.cmcrp.net/Tipperary/index.html
  Christenings, marriage and cemetery records

- Tipperary Parish Records in the Family History Library
  www.rootsweb.com/~irltip2/films.htm

- Tipperary Church of Ireland Church Registers
  www.rootsweb.com/~irltip2/coi_parishes.htm

- Quaker Records (surnames B, G & W) for County Tipperary
  www.rootsweb.com/~irltip2/quaker/index.htm

- Tipperary Parish Record Holdings
  www.rootsweb.com/~irltip2/holdings.htm
  Roman Catholic

- County Tipperary Roman Catholic Records
  www.rootsweb.com/~fianna/county/tipperary/tiprc.html
  Commencement dates only

- User Contributed Tipperary Baptisms
  www.rootsweb.com/~irltip2/bap

- User Contributed Tipperary Marriages
  www.rootsweb.com/~irltip2/tipmar/index.htm

- Marriage Records
  www.rootsweb.com/~irltip2/marriage__ndx.htm
  Various pages for Co. Tipperary

- Tipperary Family History Research
  www.tfhr.org/
  Holds the sacramental registers of the Roman Catholic Archdiocese of
  Cashel, and Diocese of Emly (46 parishes)

- Tipperary Born People Married in Victoria, Australia
  www.from-ireland.net/tipp/tippmarrs.htm

Aghnameadle
- Aghnameadle Church of Ireland Baptisms
  www.rootsweb.com/irltip2/aghnameadle__bap.htm
  Also marriages & burials, 19th c.

Borrisoleigh
- Borrisoleigh RC Parish Marriages 1815-1900
  www.connorsgenealogy.com/tipp/BorrisoleighMarriages.htm
  Index

Carrick on Suir
- Births Registered in Carrick-On-Suir, Tipperary 1871
  www.geocities.com/irishancestralpages/cosbi1871.html

- Baptisms, Carrick-on-Suir: extracts from the Roman Catholic Parochial
  Registers of Carrick-on-Suir, 1788-1851
  www.rootsweb.com/~irltip2/carrick__bap.htm

- Some Marriages from Carrick-on-Suir 1788-1805
  www.rootsweb.com/~irltip2/carrick__mar.htm

Clonmel
- Clonmel Births: extracts from the Roman Catholic Parochial Registers
  of St. Mary's (Clonmel, Tipperary), 1837-1855
  www.rootsweb.com/~irltip2/clonbirths.htm

- [Clonmel Births 1864-79]
  freepages.genealogy.rootsweb.com/~irish/clonmel/clonbirt.htm

Tyrone
- Church Records by Parish
  freepages.genealogy.rootsweb.com/~cotyroneireland/
  churchrecord/parishrecords.html

- County Tyrone Roman Catholic Records
  www.rootsweb.com/~fianna/county/tyrone/tyrrc.html

- Tyrone County Roman Catholic Parish Records, Ireland: Baptismal and
  Marriage Parish Record Index
  www.from-ireland.net/parishrecords/tyr/tyrindexrc.htm

- Born in County Tyrone, Buried Elsewhere
  freepages.genealogy.rootsweb.com/~cotyroneireland/
  bornburied/bornburied.html
  World-wide in scope

Arboe
- Arboe Roman Catholic Baptism Records
  freepages.genealogy.rootsweb.com/~tyrone/church/churchrec/
  arboe-rc-bapt.html

  19th c.

Castlederg
- Castlederg New Cemetery Burial Records
  freepages.genealogy.rootsweb.com/~cotyroneireland/burial/
  castlederg.html

  1931-59

Coagh
- Coagh Civil Births
  freepages.genealogy.rootsweb.com/~cotyroneireland/births/
  coagh.html

  Late 19th c.

- Coagh Roman Catholic Baptism Records
  freepages.genealogy. Rootsweb.com/~cotyroneireland/births/
  coagh-rc.html

Donagheady
- Second Donagheady Presbyterian Church Marriages 1838-1845
  freepages.genealogy.rootsweb.com/~cotyroneireland/
  churchrecord/donagheadymar1838-45.html
  Continued 1845-1926 at /donagheadymar1845+.html

Donemana
- Donemana Records
  freepages.genealogy.rootsweb.com/~cotyroneireland/
  churchrecord/donemana.html
- Transcription of Donemana Presbyterian Registers
  freepages.genealogy.rootsweb.com/~cotyroneireland/
  churchrecord/donemanapresbreg.html
  Covers 1861-89

Dromore
- Dromore Roman Catholic Church Records
  freepages.genealogy.rootsweb.com/~cotyroneireland/
  churchrecord/dromorerc.html
  19th c.

Kildress
- Kildress Roman Catholic Church Records
  freepages.genealogy.rootsweb.com/~cotyroneireland/
  churchrecord/kildressrc.htm
  Baptisms, 19th c.

Killyman
- Baptisms
  freepages.genealogy.rootsweb.com/~cotyroneireland/
  churchrecord/killymanbaptisms.html
  18-19th c., index
- Killyman Burial Records
  freepages.genealogy.rootsweb.com/~tyrone/church/
  churchrec/killyman-bur.htm
  Covers 1837-62

- Killyman Baptism Records
  freepages.genealogy.rootsweb.com/~cotyroneireland/
  churchrecord/killyman.html
  Covers 1849-70
- [Killyman Marriages, Church of Ireland, 1753-1844]
  freepages.genealogy.rootsweb.com/~cotyroneireland/
  churchrecord/killymanmariiages.html
- Killyman Burial Records
  freepages.genealogy.rootsweb.com/~cotyroneireland/
  churchrecord/killyman2.html
  Covers 1837-62

Leckpatrick
- Leckpatrick Presbyterian Church Marriages 1843-1930
  freepages.genealogy.rootsweb.com/~cotyroneireland/
  churchrecord/leckpresmar1843-1930.html

Magheramason
- Magheramason Presbyterian Church Marriages, 1881-1927
  freepages.genealogy.rootsweb.com/~cotyroneireland/
  churchrecord/magheramason1881-1927.html

Pomeroy
- County Tyrone Roman Catholic Parish Records, Ireland: Pomeroy
  www.from-ireland.net/parishrecords/tyr/pomeroy.htm
  Includes baptisms, 1869-72

Waterford
- County Waterford CMC Record Project
  www.cmcrp.net/Waterford/index.html
- Waterford Church of Ireland Church Registers
  www.rootsweb.com/~irlwat2/cofi.htm
- County Waterford Roman Catholic Records
  www.rootsweb.com/~fianna/county/waterford/watrc.html
  Commencement dates only

Waterford
- Baptisms and Marriages of Newfoundlanders performed at St. Patrick's
  Church, Waterford, Ireland, period of 1752-1770
  ngb.chebucto.org/Parish/bap-mar-waterford-1752-1770.shtml

Westmeath
- County Westmeath Roman Catholic Records
  www.rootsweb.com/~fianna/county/westmeath/wemrc.html

Mullingar
- Church of Ireland Records: Mullingar 1877-1900
  www.rootsweb.com/~irlwem2/mullingar/mullingar.htm
  Index to baptisms and marriages

Wexford
- County Wexford CMC Record Project
  www.cmcrp.net/Wexford/index.html

- Wexford County Roman Catholic Parish Records, Ireland: Baptismal and
  Marriage Parish Record Index
  www.from-ireland.net/parishrecords/wex/wexrcindex.htm

New Ross
- Wexford County Roman Catholic Parish Records, Ireland: New Ross
  www.from-ireland.net/parishrecords/wex/nrbapindex1.htm
  See also /nrextracts.htm

Wicklow
- County Wicklow CMC Record Project
  www.cmcrp.net/Wicklow/index.html
  Christenings, marriages and cemetery records

- County Wicklow Church of Ireland Records
  www.rootsweb.com/~fianna/county/wicklow/wiccoi.html

- County Wicklow Methodist Presbyterian and Quaker Records
  www.rootsweb.com/~fianna/county/wicklow/wicprot.html

- County Wicklow Roman Catholic Records
  www.rootsweb.com/~fianna/county/wicklow/wicrc.html

Arklow
- Peggy Leonards Christening Records of Arklow Parish, Wicklow
  www.cmcrp.net/Wicklow/ArklowB1.htm
  Index, 19-20th c.

- County Wicklow: Arklow Parish Marriage Records
  www.cmcrp.net/Wicklow/ArklowM1.htm
  Index, 18-20th c.

Dunganstown
- Search Dunganstown Parish Records, Wicklow, Ireland, Baptisms
  1842-1910
  www.ancestorsatrest.com/church_records/
  dunganstown_parish_register_wicklow.shtml

10. Monumental Inscriptions

Introductions

- Cemetary Records
  www.rootsweb.com/~fianna/guide/cemetary.html
  Brief introduction

- Cemeteries of Ireland
  www.interment.net/ireland
  Numerous transcriptions of records, mostly listed below

- Guide to Gravestone Inscriptions
  www.proni.gov.uk/records/graves.htm

- Gravestone Records
  scripts.ireland.com/ancestor/browse/records/graveyard
  Introduction to sources in the Public Record Office of Northern Ireland

- International Association of Jewish Genealogical Societies: Cemetery Project: Ireland (Republic of Ireland and Northern Ireland)
  www.jewishgen.org/cemetery/brit/ireland.html

- Saving Graves Ireland
  www.savinggraves-uk.org/ireland/
  Preservation and restoration of graveyards

- Understanding the Stones
  www.proni.gov.uk/records/stones.htm

- Ireland
  www.mbs-brasses.co.uk/bibliography__Foreign.htm#Ireland
  Bibliography of monumental brasses

Databases & Collections

- Cemetery Headstone Transcription
  members.webone.com.au/~sgrieves/cemeteries__ireland.htm
  Collection of inscriptions from Cos. Tipperary, Waterford, Leitrim & Londonderry

- Death Records for Ireland on Ancestors at Rest
  ancestorsatrest.com/ireland__genealogy.shtml
  Scroll down. Monumental inscriptions from various cemeteries; also various extracts from registers *etc*.

- Find a Grave
  www.findagrave.com
  Click on 'Search for a cemetery', and search 'Ireland' for lists of transcriptions from over 200 Irish cemeteries. Mostly a small number from each cemetery, but some substantial transcriptions are listed separately below.

- Irish Gravestone Inscriptions
  content.ancestry.com/iexec/?htx=BookList&dbid=49207
  Subscription required

- Irish War Memorials
  www.irishwarmemorials.ie

- History from Headstones
  www.historyfromheadstones.com/
  Database of 50,000+ Northern Ireland monumental inscriptions

- Irelands Gravestone Index
  www.irishgenealogy.ie/frame__1024.cfm
  Nearly 400,000 inscriptions from 851 cemeteries in ten Irish counties, and growing (mainly Northern Ireland)

- Memorials of the Dead
  www.irishfamilyresearch.co.uk/mems.htm
  8000 memorial inscriptions. Subscription required.

- Churches & Cemeteries
  homepage.eircom.net/%7Ekevm/Churches.htm
  Pages for 23 places in various counties, mostly listed individually below

- Gravestone Transcriptions
  www.from-ireland.net/contents/graves.htm
  Numerous pages of transcriptions, mostly listed below

- Irish Cemetery Records
  www.scotlandsclans.com/ircemeteries.htm
  Links to numerous transcripts of inscriptions, etc.

- Irish Memorials of Dead
  www.ajmorris.com/dig/toc/memdead.htm
  Pay per view site. Index to tombstone inscriptions collected in the 19th c.

County and Local Pages

Antrim

- Antrim Gravestone Inscriptions
  scripts.ireland.com/ancestor/browse/counties/ulster/antrim5.htm
  List of published transcripts

Aughnahoy

- Aughnahoy
  www.from-ireland.net/graves/aughnahoyantrim.htm
  Inscriptions

Belfast

- Monumental Inscriptions, Belfast Charitable Institution Burying
  Ground, Belfast, Co. Antrim
  ancestorsatrest.com/cemetery__records/belfast-cemetery.shtml

Billy

- Gravestone Inscriptions at the Old Burying Ground Beside Billy Parish
  Church in North Antrim
  www.rootsweb.com/~irlantbp

Dundonald

- Dundonald Cemetery
  www.findagrave.com
  Click on 'search for a cemetery', search for 'Ireland', and scroll down
  to 'Dundonald'

Layde

- Layde Graveyard
  www.from-ireland.net/graves/taydeantrim.htm
  Inscriptions

Rasharkin

- Rasharkin Church of Ireland Graveyard Inscriptions
  www.4qd.org/bann/church/RasharkinCOI/graveyard.html

Roselawn

- Roselawn Cemetery
  www.findagrave.com
  Click on 'Search for a cemetery', search 'Ireland', and scroll down to
  'Roselawn'

Armagh

Armagh

- Gravestone Inscriptions, Sandy Hill Graveyard, Armagh City
  www.from-ireland.net/graves/sandyhillarmagh.htm

Creggan

- Inscriptions in Creggan Graveyard
  www.from-ireland.net/graves/cregganarmagh.htm

Crossmaglen

- Creggan Graveyard in Crossmaglen, Armagh County
  www.from-ireland.net/graves/creggancrossmaglenant.htm

Tartaragha

- Tartaragha Old Graveyards, alias the Toby Hole
  www.geocities.com/craigavonhs/rev/flemingtartaghan.html

Carlow

- County Carlow Gravestone Inscriptions
  www.rootsweb.com/~irlcar2/inscriptions.htm

- Carlow Old Graves
  www.rootsweb.com/~irlcar2/Old__Graves.htm

- Miscellaneous County Carlow Inscriptions
  www.from-ireland.net/graves/carlowmisc.htm

- USA/Canada Gravestone Inscriptions
  www.rootsweb.com/~irlcar2/usa__canada.htm
  Commemorating people from Co. Carlow

Bennekerry

- Saint Mary Churchyard, Bennekerry, County Carlow, Ireland
  www.interment.net/data/ireland/carlow/stmary__benn/index.htm

Carlow

- County Carlow Memorial Inscriptions: St. Mary's Church of Ireland,
  Carlow
  www.rootsweb.com/~irlcar2/St__Marys__CoI.htm

Dunleckney
- Carlow: Dunleckney Cemetery: Some Tombstone Inscriptions
  www.ajmorris.com/dig/fap/rec/
  Click on title. Registration needed

Graiguecullen
- Killeshin Church of Ireland, Graiguecullen
  www.rootsweb.com/~irlcar2/church__of__ire__graigue.htm

Hacketstown
- County Carlow Memorial Inscriptions: Hacketstown Cemetery
  www.rootsweb.com/~irlcar2/Hacketstown__Cemetery.htm
  See also /hacketstown__ins.htm

- Hacketstown Cemetery, Hacketstown, County Carlow, Ireland
  www.interment.net/data/ireland/carlow/hacketstown/hacket.htm

Killerig
- County Carlow Memorial Inscriptions, Killerig & Tullow Churchyards
  www.rootsweb.com/~irlcar2/memorials.htm

Old Leighlin
- Saint Lazerian Churchyard, Old Leighlin, County Carlow, Ireland
  www.interment.net/data/ireland/carlow/lazerian

- County Carlow Memorial Inscriptions: St. Laserian's Cathedral, Old Leighlin, County Carlow
  www.rootsweb.com/~irlcar2/st__lazerians__church.htm

Rathvilly
- Saint Mary Church of Ireland Cemetery, Rathvilly, County Carlow, Ireland
  www.interment.net/data/ireland/carlow/stmary/mary.htm

Tullow
- Mullawn Cemetery, Tullow, County Carlow, Ireland
  www.interment.net/data/ireland/carlow/mullawn/mullawn.htm

- Mullawn Cemetery, Tullow, County Carlow, Ireland
  www.interment.net/data/ireland/carlow/mullawn/mullawn.htm

- Saint Patrick Cemetery, Tullow, County Carlow, Ireland
  www.interment.net/data/ireland/carlow/patrick/index.htm

Cavan
- County Cavan Gravestone Inscriptions
  www.rootsweb.com/~fianna/county/cavan/cavtomb.html
  List of transcripts

Ballyhaise
- Baillyhaise Cemetery
  www.sierratel.com/colinf/genuki/CAV/Castleterra/
  BallyhaiseCemetery.html
  List of family plots

Killeshandra
- Inscriptions in Killeshandra Old Cemetery
  homepages.iol.ie/~galwill/histtomb.htm

Knocktemple
- Knocktemple Old Cemetery Inscriptions, County Cavan, Ireland
  www.ancestry.com/search/rectype/inddbs/4225.htm

Maghera
- Maghera Cemetery, County Cavan, Ireland
  www.interment.net/data/ireland/cavan/maghera/maghera.htm

Mountnugent
- Ballinacree RC Churchyard, Mountnugent, County Cavan, Ireland
  www.interment.net/data/ireland/cavan/ballinacree/index.htm

Mullagh
- Saint Killian Churchyard, Mullagh, County Cavan, Ireland
  www.interment.net/data/ireland/cavan/killian

- Teampall Cheallaigh Cemetery, Mullagh, County Cavan, Ireland
  www.interment.net/data/ireland/cavan/teampall__heallaigh/
  teampall.htm

Templeport
- Inscriptions in Templeport Cemetery
  www.stpeter.utvinternet.com/headstones.htm
  See also /memorialindex.htm

Virginia
- Church of Ireland Churchyard, Virginia, County Cavan, Ireland
  www.interment.net/data/ireland/cavan/coi__virginia

- Derver Graveyard, Virginia, County Cavan, Ireland
  www.interment.net/data/ireland/cavan/derver/index.htm

- The Old Cemetery, Virginia, County Cavan, Ireland
  www.interment.net/data/ireland/cavan/old

- Raffony Graveyard, Virginia, County Cavan, Ireland
  www.interment.net/data/ireland/cavan/raffony/raffony.htm

Clare
- Graveyard Inscriptions
  www.rootsweb.com/~irlcla/graveyardinscriptions.html
  Surname index to transcriptions at the East Clare Heritage Centre

- Memorials of the Dead, West Clare
  www.from-ireland.net/graves/clarewestgraves.htm
  Surname index to published transcriptions

Doolin
- Holy Rosary Cemetery, Doolin, County Clare, Ireland
  www.interment.net/data/ireland/clare/rosary

Ennis
- Drumcliffe Cemetery, Ennis, County Clare, Ireland
  www.interment.net/data/ireland/clare/drumcliff/drumcliff.htm

- Kilmaley Cemetery, Kilmaley, Ennis, County Clare
  www.interment.net/data/ireland/clare/kilmaley/kilmaley.htm

- Kilnamona Cemetery, Ennis, County Clare, Ireland
  www.interment.net/data/ireland/clare/kilnamona/kilnamona.htm

Ennistymon
- Killernan Cemetery, Ennistymon, County Clare, Ireland
  www.interment.net/data/ireland/clare/killernan/killernan.htm

- Kilshanny Cemetery, Ennistymon, County Clare, Ireland
  www.interment.net/data/ireland/clare/kilshanny/shanny.htm

- Moughna Cemetery, Ennistymon, County Clare, Ireland
  www.interment.net/data/ireland/clare/moughna

- Old Cemetery, Ennistymon, County Clare, Ireland
  www.interment.net/data/ireland/clare/oldcem/oldcem.htm

Inagh
- Inagh Cemetery, County Clare, Ireland
  www.interment.net/data/ireland/clare/inagh/inagh.htm

Killard
- Cemetery Inscriptions: Doonbeg and Clohanes, Killard Parish, Co. Clare
  freepages.genealogy.rootsweb.com/~msjenkins/records/clarecem.htm

Kilmurry East
- Kilmurry McMahon Graveyard, Kilmurry East, County Clare, Ireland
  www.interment.net/data/ireland/clare/mcmahon

Kilrush
- Breffa Cemetery, Kilrush, County Clare, Ireland
  www.interment.net/data/ireland/clare/breffa

- Doonbeg Cemetery, Kilrush, County Clare, Ireland
  www.interment.net/data/ireland/clare/doonbeg/doon.htm

- Kilmurry Ibrickane Cemetery, Kilrush, County Clare, Ireland
  www.interment.net/data/ireland/clare/killmurray

- New Shanakyle Cemetery, Kilrush, County Clare, Ireland
  www.interment.net/data/ireland/clare/new__shan

- Shanakyle Old Graveyard Kilrush, County Clare, Ireland
  www.interment.net/data/ireland/clare/shanakyle

Labasheeda
- Killofin Cemetery, Labasheeda, County Clare, Ireland
  www.interment.net/data/ireland/clare/killofin

Lahinch
- Callura Cemetery, Lahinch, County Clare, Ireland
  www.interment.net/data/ireland/clare/callura

- Saint Mary Churchyard, Moy, Lahinch, County Clare, Ireland
  www.interment.net/data/ireland/clare/stmary/stmary.htm

Liscannor
- Kilmacreehy Cemetery, Liscannor, County Clare, Ireland
  www.interment.net/data/ireland/clare/kilmacreehy

- Saint Bridget's Well Cemetery, Liscannor, County Clare, Ireland
  www.interment.net/data/ireland/clare/stbridget/bridget.htm

Miltown Malbay
- Ballard Graveyard, Miltown Malbay, County Clare, Ireland
  www.interment.net/data/ireland/clare/ballard/ballard.htm

- Kilfarboy Cemetery, Miltown Malbay, County Clare, Ireland
  www.interment.net/data/ireland/clare/kilfarboy/kilfarboy.htm

Mullagh
- County Clare, Ireland: Mullagh - Quilty Graveyard Photos
  www.rootsweb.com/~irlcla/Mullaghgraveyard.html

Quilty
See Mullagh

Tulla
- Tulla Cemetery, Tulla, County Clare, Ireland
  www.interment.net/data/ireland/clare/tulla

Cork
- Cork Gravestone Inscriptions
  scripts.ireland.com/ancestor/browse/counties/munster/cork5.htm
  List of transcripts

- Cork Graveyards and Published Transcriptions
  freepages.genealogy.rootsweb.com/~colin/Ireland/
  CorkGraveyards.htm

- County Cork Cemeteries and Gravestones
  myhome.ispdr.net.au/~mgrogan/cork/a__cemetery.htm
  Collections of pages

- [Gravestones from various Cemeteries in West Cork]
  www.ginnisw.com/Graves/Thumb/Thumbs1.htm

Adrigole
- Adrigole Memorial Inscriptions, R.C.
  www.from-ireland.net/graves/adrigoletrans.htm
  Inscriptions

Aghinagh
- Cork Gravestones Name Index: Aghinagh
  www.from-ireland.net/graves/aghinaghindex.htm

Ahiohill
See Murragh

Berehaven
- Berehaven Tombstone Inscriptions, Co. Cork
  myhome.ispdr.net.au/~mgrogan/cork/berehaven.htm

Carrigrohanebeg
- Cork Gravestones Index to Names: Carrigrohanebeg
  www.from-ireland.net/graves/carrigrohanebegindex.htm

Castletown
- [Gravestones from Castletown and Kinneigh, County Cork]
  www.ginnisw.com/Ireland%20Trip%202001/
  Kinneigh%20and%20Castletown%20Graves/Thumb/Thumb1.htm

Churchtown
See Doneraile

Clonmult
- Cork Gravestones Name Index: Clonmult
  www.from-ireland.net/graves/clonmultindex.htm

Dangandonovan
- Cork Gravestones Name Index: Dangandonovan
  www.from-ireland.net/graves/dangandonindex.htm

- Dangandonovan Cemetery
  myhome.ispdr.net.au/~mgrogan/cork/dangandonovan.htm

Doneraile
- Cemetery Inscriptions from Casey vol.11. Old Court Cemetery, Doneraile, Granard Cemetery, Liscarroll, Killabraher, Parish of Dromina, Exterior of Churchtown Church; Kilbrogan Cemetery, Co. Cork
  myhome.ispdr.net.au/~mgrogan/cork/donraile.htm

Dromina
See Doneraile

Frankfield
- Frankfield Cemetery Inscriptions
  www.scotlandsclans.com/frankfield.htm

Kilbehenny
- Kilbehenny Grave Inscriptions, Co. Cork
  myhome.ispdr.net.au/~mgrogan/cork/kilbehenny.htm

Kilbrogan
See Doneraile

Killabraher
See Doneraile

Killeagh
- Cork Gravestones Name Index: Killeagh
  www.from-ireland.net/graves/killeaghindex.htm

- Killeagh Cemetery
  myhome.ispdr.net.au/~mgrogan/cork/killeagh_cem.htm

- Gravestone Inscriptions, Killeagh Burial Ground, Co.Cork
  myhome.ispdr.net.au/~mgrogan/cork/killeagh_grave.htm

Kilnaglory
- The Gravestone Inscriptions of Co. Cork, V: Kilnaglory Burial Ground
  www.from-ireland.net/graves/kilnaglorycork.htm
  Index to published transcription

Kinneagh
See Castletown

Liscarrol
See Doneraile

Mallow
- Grave Monuments, St. James Protestant Cemetery, Mallow, Co. Cork
  myhome.ispdr.net.au/~mgrogan/cork/mallow_stj.htm

- Monument Inscriptions from St. Mary's Catholic Cemetery, Mallow, Co. Cork
  myhome.ispdr.net.au/~mgrogan/cork/mallow_stm_grave.htm

Midleton
- [Gravestones from Midleton, Co. Cork]
  **www.ginnisw.com/Ireland%20Trip%202001/
  Midleton%20Graves/Thumb/Thumbs1.htm**

Mologga
- Mologga Cemetery Inscriptions, Co. Cork
  myhome.ispdr.net.au/~mgrogan/cork/mologga.htm

Murragh
- [Gravestones from Old Murragh Cemetery and Ahiohill Cemetery]
  **www.ginnisw.com/Ireland%20Trip%202001/
  Murragh%20and%20Ahiohill%20Cemetery/Thumb/Thumbs1.htm**

Rosscarbery
- Partial Transcriptions from the Old Cemetery in Rosscarbery Town
  www.failteromhat.com/rosscem.htm

Tisaxon
- The Gravestone Inscriptions of Co. Cork, VII. Tisaxon Burial Ground
  www.from-ireland.net/graves/tisaxoncork.htm
  Index to published transcription

Donegal
- Cemeteries of Donegal
  freepages.genealogy.rootsweb.com/~donegaleire/Cemeteries.html

- Monumental Inscriptions
  freepages.genealogy.routsweb.com/~donegal/mis.htm
  General discussion with links to Donegal sites

Ballyshannon

- The Gravestone Inscriptions, St. Anne's Church of Ireland, Ballyshannon
  freepages.genealogy.rootsweb.com/~donegal/stanne.htm

- St. Anne's Church of Ireland, Ballyshannon, County Donegal, Ireland
  www.interment.net/data/ireland/donegal/st__anne.htm

- The Gravestone Inscriptions St. Annes Church of Ireland, Ballyshannon
  www.ulsterancestry.com/ua-free__GravestoneInscriptions.html

- Assaroe Abbey Cemetery, Ballyshannon
  freepages.genealogy.rootsweb.com/~donegal/assaroecem.htm

- Assaroe Abbey Cemetery, Ballyshannon
  www.ulsterancestry.com/
  Abbey__Cemetery__Inscriptions-Assaroe%20.html

Bundoran

- Finner, Bundoran
  freepages.genealogy.rootsweb.com/~donegal/finner.htm
  Monumental inscriptions

- Finner Graveyard, Bundoran, County Donegal
  www.interment.net/data/donegal/finner__graveyard.htm

Creeslough

- County Donegal, Ireland, Catholic Cemetery: Creeslough, County Donegal, Ireland
  freepages.genealogy.rootsweb.com/~donegaleire/Doncem.html

- Creeslough Cemetery
  freepages.genealogy.rootsweb.com/~donegaleire/Creescem.html

Gartan

- Gartan Graveyard, County Donegal, Ireland
  www.interment.net/data/ireland/donegal/gartan__graveyard.htm

- The Gravestone Inscriptions, Gartan Graveyard
  freepages.genealogy.rootsweb.com/~donegal/gartan/gartgrave.htm

Glenfin

- Kilteevogue Cemetery, Glenfin, County Donegal, Ireland
  www.interment.net/data/ireland/donegal/kilteevogue

Glenswilly

- Glenswilly Cemetery
  freepages.genealogy.rootsweb.com/~donegal/gartan/glenswilcem.htm

Gortahork

- Gortahork Cemetery
  freepages.genealogy.rootsweb.com/~donegal/gortcem.htm

Inishowen

- Cemeteries and Graveyards in Inishowen, Donegal: Malin Presbyterian Church
  freepages.genealogy.rootsweb.com/~donegal/inishowencem.htm

- Cemeteries and Graveyards in Inishowen, Donegal: Moville Presbyterian & Church of Ireland Cemeteries
  freepages.genealogy.rootsweb.com/~donegal/inishowencem2.htm

- Cemeteries and Graveyards in Inishowen, Donegal: Redcastle Church of Ireland Cemetery
  freepages.genealogy.rootsweb.com/~donegal/inishowencem3.htm

Inver

- Inver C.O.I. Cemetery
  freepages.genealogy.rootsweb.com/%7Edonegaleire/Inver.html

Iskaheen

- St. Patrick's, Iskaheen (Old Graveyard)
  freepages.genealogy.rootsweb.com/~donegal/stpatistaheen.htm

Killeshandra

- Inscriptions in Killeshandra Old Cemetery
  www.iol.ie/~galwill/histtomb.htm

Killaghtee

- Old Killaghtee Cemetery
  freepages.genealogy.rootsweb.com/~donegaleire/Killa.html

Letterkenny

- Leck Cemetery, Letterkenny, Donegal, Ireland
  freepages.genealogy.rootsweb.com/~donegaleire/Donleck.htm
  Gravestone Inscriptions

Lettermacaward
- Headstone Inscriptions from St. Bridget's Cemetery, Toome, Lettermacaward
  freepages.genealogy.rootsweb.com/~donegal/lettermacem.htm

Malin
See Inishowen

Moville
See Inishowen

Pettigo
- Carne Graveyard, Pettigo, Co. Donegal
  www.rootsweb.com/~nirfer2/Documents/Cemeteries/
          Carne__Cemetery__1.doc

Redcastle
See Inishowen

Templecrone
- St. Mary's Kincasslagh Cemetery, Templecrone, Co. Donegal: Headstone Inscriptions
  freepages.genealogy.rootsweb.com/~donegal/stmarysk.htm

Templedouglas
- Templedouglas Graveyard
  freepages.genealogy.rootsweb.com/~donegal/gartan/templedgy.htm

Termon
- St. Columba's Church, Termon & Gartan
  freepages.genealogy.rootsweb.com/~donegal/gartan/
          termongartan.htm

Tullaghobegley
- Tullaghobegley Graveyard
  freepages.genealogy.rootsweb.com/~donegal/tullagrave.htm

- Magheragallon Old Graveyard, Tullaghobegley
  freepages.genealogy.rootsweb.com/~donegal/magheracem.htm

Down
- County Down Burial Index 1700s
  www.rootsweb.com/~nirdow2/Burial/down__index.htm
  Inscriptions

- County Down Graveyard Transcriptions Volume 2
  www.from-ireland.net/graves/downvol2.htm
  From 9 graveyards

- Down Gravestone Inscriptions
  scripts.ireland.com/ancestor/browse/counties/ulster/down5.htm
  List of published inscriptions

- Churches and Graveyards of Co. Down
  freepages.genealogy.rootsweb.com/~rosdavies/CHURCHES/A-I.htm
  Continued at /K__W.htm
  List

Aghlisnafin
- Selected Tombstone Inscriptions from Aghlisnafin, County Down
  www.ajmorris.com/dig/fap/rec/
  Registration needed. Click on title

Ballycopeland
See also Millisle
- Ballycopeland Presbyterian Cemetery
  www.yorick.plus.com/Ballycopeland/FrameSet.htm

Ballywalter
- County Down: Whitechurch Cemetery, Ballywalter
  www.yorick.plus.com/Whitechurch/FrameSet.htm

Bangor Abbey
- Bangor Abbey Church
  www.yorick.plus.com/yorick2/BangorAbbey/FrameSet.htm

Donaghadee
- Donaghadee Parish Headstones
  www.yorick.plus.com/Donaghadee/FrameSet.htm

- Templepatrick Graveyard, Miller Hill, Donaghadee
  www.yorick.plus.com/Gravestones/FrameSet.htm

Donaghcloney
- Donaghcloney Presbyterian Graveyard Inscriptions
  www.ulsterancestry.com/ShowFreePage/php?id=202

Greyabbey
- Greyabbey Graveyard, Down
  www.yorick.plus.com/Greyabbey/FrameSet.htm

Millisle
- Millisle & Ballycopeland Presbyterian Church
  www.yorick.plus.com/Millisle/FrameSet.htm

Dublin
- Gravestone Inscriptions
  scripts.ireland.com/ancestor/browse/counties/leinster/dublin5.htm
  List of published transcripts for Co. Dublin

Ballbriggan
- Saints Peter and Paul Cemetery, County Dublin, Ireland
  www.interment.net/data/ireland/dublin/saintspp/saintspp.htm
  At Ballbriggan

Blackrock
- Dean's Grange Monumental Inscriptions, Blackrock, Dublin, Ireland
  ancestorsatrest.com/cemetery__record/deans-grange-cemetery.shtml

Castleknock
- Abbotstown Castleknock, County Dublin, Ireland
  ancestorsatrest.com/cemetery__records/
  abbotstown__castleknock.shtml
- St. Bridgid Church of Ireland Cemetery, Castleknock, County Dublin, Ireland
  www.interment.net/data/ireland/dublin/stbridgid

Clonsilla
- Saint Mary Churchyard, Clonsilla, County Dublin, Ireland
  www.interment.net/data/ireland/dublin/stmary

Deans Grange
- Deans Grange Cemetery, County Dublin, Ireland
  www.interment.net/data/ireland/dublin/deans/dean__grange.htm

Donabate
- Saint Patrick Cemetery, Donabate, County Dublin, Ireland
  www.interment.net/data/ireland/dublin/stpat/stpat.htm

Dublin
- Names on Coffin Plates in the Vaults of St. Andrews Church, Westland Row, Dublin (R.C.)
  www.from-ireland.net/graves/standrewswestlandrowdublin.htm
- Saint Patrick's Cathedral
  www.findagrave.com
  Click on 'Search for a cemetery', search 'Ireland', and scroll down to 'Saint Patrick's Cathedral'. At Dublin

Garrisontown
- Ballmadun Cemetery, Garrisontown, County Dublin, Ireland
  www.interment.net/data/ireland/dublin/ballmadun
- Garrisontown Cemetery, Garrisontown, County Dublin, Ireland
  www.interment.net/data/ireland/dublin/garrisontown

Glasnevin
- Glasnevin Cemetery
  www.glasnevin-cemetery.ie/
  Includes details of a project to create a database for 250,000 burial records. Click on 'The Cemetery' and 'Project'.
- Glasnevin Cemetery
  en.wikipedia.org/wiki/Glasnevin__Cemetery
  Encyclopedia article
- Glasnevin Cemetery
  www.findagrave.com
  Click on 'search for a cemetery', search 'Ireland', scroll down to 'Glasnevin'.
- Glasnevin Cemetery, County Dublin, Ireland
  www.interment.net/data/ireland/dublin/glasnevin/glasnevin.htm
- Glasnevin Cemetery, Dublin
  www.from-ireland.net/graves/glasnevin.htm
  Transcription of 190+ inscriptions

Grallagh

- Grallagh Cemetery, Grallagh, County Dublin, Ireland
  www.interment.net/data/ireland/dublin/grallagh/grallagh.htm

Grangegorman

- Grangegorman Military Cemetery, County Dublin, Ireland
  www.interment.net/data/ireland/dublin/grangegorman/

Howth

- Memorial Inscriptions, Church of the Assumption (earlier
  St. Mary's RC)
  freepages.genealogy.rootsweb.com/~chrisu/howth2.htm

Kilternan

- Kilternan Church of Ireland Cemetery, Kilternan, County Dublin,
  Ireland
  www.interment.net/data/ireland/dublin/kilternan

Lusk

- Lusk Old Churchyard Cemetery, County Dublin, Ireland
  www.interment.net/data/ireland/dublin/oldlusk/

- Saint Macullin Churchyard, County Dublin, Ireland
  www.interment.net/data/ireland/dublin/macullin/macullin.htm
  At Lusk

Mulhuddart

- Mulhuddart Cemetery, County Dublin, Ireland
  www.interment.net/data/ireland/dublin/mulhuddart/mulhuddart.htm

Rush

- Kenure Cemetery, Rush, County Dublin, Ireland
  www.interment.net/data/ireland/dublin/kenure/kenure.htm

- Whitestown Cemetery, Rush, County Dublin, Ireland
  www.interment.net/data/dublin/whitestown/whitestown.htm

Skerries

- St. Patricks Holmpatrick Cemetery, Skerries, County Dublin, Ireland
  www.interment.net/data/ireland/dublin/patrick/holmpatrick.htm

Sutton

- Kilbarrack Cemetery, Sutton, County Dublin, Ireland
  www.interment.net/data/ireland/dublin/kilbarrack

- Saint Fintan Cemetery, Sutton, County Dublin, Ireland
  www.interment.net/data/ireland/dublin/stfintan

Swords Village

- Saint Colmcille Churchyard, Swords Village, County Dublin, Ireland
  www.interment.net/data/ireland/dublin/colmcille

Tallaght

- Tallaght, County Dublin, Church of Ireland
  ancestorsatrest.cemetery__records/tallaght__dublin.shtml

Fermanagh

- Fermanagh Gravestone Inscriptions
  scripts.ireland.com/ancestor/browse/counties/ulster/fermanag5.htm
  List of published transcripts

- Cemeteries of Fermanagh
  www.rootsweb.com/~nirfer/cemeteries.html
  Collections of inscriptions, some listed below

Aghalurcher

- Aghalurcher Headstones
  www.ulsterancestry.com/ShowFreePage.php?id=204

- Fermanagh Gravestones Name Index: Aghalurcher
  www.from-ireland.net/graves/aghalurcherferm.htm

Aghavea

- Fermanagh Gravestones Name Index: Aghavea
  www.from-ireland.net/graves/aghaveafermanagh.htm

Ardess

- Ardess Graveyard
  www.rootsweb.com/~nirfer/ardess2__graveyard.htm

- Ardess Graveyard
  www.rootsweb.com/~nirfer2/Documents/Cemeteries/
  Ardess__Graveyard.doc

- Ardess New Graveyard
  www.rootsweb.com/~nirfer/ardess__new__graveyard.htm

Carrick
- Carrick Graveyard
  www.rootsweb.com/~nirfer2/Documents/Cemeteries/
                              Carrick__Graveyard.doc

Clones
- [Clones Graveyard]
  www.rootsweb.com/~nirfer2/Documents/Cemeteries/
                              Clones__Graveyard.doc

- Early Memorials in Clones Round Tower Graveyard: Clones Abbey
  Graveyard and Tierney's R.C. Graveyard, Roselea
  www.rootsweb.com/~nirfer2/Documents/Cemeteries/
                              Roselea__Graveyeard.doc

Derrygonnelly
- Derrygonnelly Graveyard
  www.rootsweb.com/~nirfer2/Documents/Cemeteries/
                              Derrygonnelly-Graveyard.doc

Donagh
- Fermanagh Gravestones: Name Index: Donagh
  www.from-ireland.net/graves/donaghferm.htm

Drumully
- Drumully Cemetery
  www.rootsweb.com/~nirfer/drumullycemetery.htm

- [Drumully Graveyard]
  www.rootsweb.com/~nirfer2/Documents/Cemeteries/
                              Drumully__Cemetery.xls
  See also /Drumully__Cemetery__Notes.doc

Florencecourt
- Grave Stone Inscriptions, Florencecourt
  www.ulsterancestry.com/ShowFreePage.php?id=163

Galloon
- Inscriptions in Galoon Cemetery
  www.rootsweb.com/~nirfer2/Documents/Cemeteries/
                              Galoon__Graveyard.doc

Irvinestown
- Irvinestown: Tower Cemetery
  www.rootsweb.com/~nirfer/irvinestown__tower.htm

- [Irvinestown Tower Graveyard]
  www.rootsweb.com/~nirfer2/Documents/Cemeteries/
                              Irvinestown__Tower__Graveyard.doc

- Tower Graveyard (Irvinestown)
  www.rootsweb.com/~nirfer/tower__graveyard.htm

Kinawley
- Kinawley: Headstone Inscriptions in Kinawley Catholic Cemetery
  Co. Fermanagh
  www.ulsterancestry.com/ShowFreePage.php?id=182

Pettigo
- Pettigo Church of Ireland Graveyard
  www.rootsweb.com/~nirfer/pettigo__ci__graveyard.htm

Rosslea
See also Clones
- Fermanagh Gravestones Name Index. St. Tierney's, Rosslea
  www.from-ireland.net/graves/sttierneysferm.htm

Slavin
- Slavin Church Burial Plots, County Fermanagh
  www.rootsweb.com/~nirfer2/Documents/Cemeteries/
                              Slavin__Graveyard__Plot__List.doc
  See also /Slavin__Churchyard__Plot__Layout.xls

Tullynageeran
- Fermanagh Gravestones Name Index: Tullynageeran
  www.from-ireland.net/graves/tullynageerferman.thm

Galway

Beagh
- Inscriptions from Shanaglish, Beagh Parish, Galway
  www.celticcousins.net/ireland/cembeagh.htm

Kilbeacanty
- Old Kilbeacanty Cemetery
  www.findagrave.com
  Click on 'Search for a cemetery', search 'Ireland' and scroll down to
  'Old Kilbeacanty'.

Mullaghgloss
- Toorena Cemetery, Mullaghgloss, County Galway, Ireland
  www.interment.net/data/ireland/galway/toorena/toorena.htm

Oughterard
- Kilcummin Cemetery, Oughterard, County Galway, Ireland
  www.interment.net/data/ireland/galway/kilcummin

Portumna
- Christchurch Churchyard, Portumna, County Galway, Ireland
  www.interment.net/ireland/galway/christchurch

Renvyle
- Renvyle Cemetery, Renvyle, County Galway, Ireland
  www.interment.net/data/ireland/galway/renvyle/renvyle.htm

Kerry
- Kerry Gravestones
  scripts.ireland.com/ancestor/browse/counties/munster/Kerry5.htm
  List of published transcripts

- Gravestone Inscriptions of Kerry Emigrants, St. Brigid's Cemetery,
  Hadley, MA
  www.rootsweb.com/~irlker/hdleygrave.html

Brosna
- Brosna Cemetery Inscriptions
  www.geocities.com/bluegumtrees/cemetery.html

Killorglin
- Killorglin Tombstone Inscriptions
  www.rootsweb.com/~irlker/tombkillor.html

Knockbrack
- Burial Ground, Knockbrack
  www.from-ireland/net/graves/knockbrackinscrs.htm

Listowel
- Cemetery Inscriptions: Listowel Area
  www.rootsweb.com/~irlker/tomblist.html

Milltown
- Milltown Tombstone Inscriptions
  www.rootsweb.com/~irlker/tombmilltown.html

Tralee
- Tralee War Memorial
  www.rootsweb.com/~irlker/traleewarmem.html

Valentia Island
- Headstone Inscriptions on Valentia Island: Kylemore Burial Grounds
  www.rootsweb.com/~irlker/cemkylemore.html

Kildare
- Gravestone Inscriptions
  scripts.ireland.com/ancestor/browse/counties/leinster/Kildare5.htm
  List of transcripts for Co. Kildare

Ballymore Eustace
- Saint Mary Cemetery, Ballymore Eustace, County Kildare, Ireland
  www.interment.net/data/ireland/kildare/stmary/mary.htm

Bodenstown
- Bodenstown Churchyard Cemetery, Bodenstown, County Kildare, Ireland
  www.interment.net/data/ireland/kildare/bodenstown/
  bodenstown.htm

Celbridge
- Ladychapel Cemetery, Celbridge, County Kildare, Ireland
  www.interment.net/data/ireland/kildare/ladychapel/lady.htm

Clane
- Clane Abbey Cemetery, Clane Village, County Kildare, Ireland
  www.interment.net/data/ireland/kildare/clane__abbey/clane.htm

Eadestown
- Eadestown Cemetery, Eadestown, County Kildare, Ireland
  www.interment.net/data/ireland/kildare/easdestown/eadestown.htm

Enfield
- Kilshanroe Cemetery, Enfield, County Kildare
  www.interment.net/data/ireland/kildare/kilshanroe/kilshanroe.htm

Killybegs
- Kildare Gravestones Name Index: Killybegs, Old: Prosperous,
  Co. Kildare
  www.from-ireland.net/graves/kild/killybegs.htm

Naas
- Kildare Gravestones Name Index: St. David's, Naas, Co. Kildare
  www.from-ireland.net/graves/kild/stdavidsnaas.htm

Kilkenny
- Gravestone Inscriptions
  www.kilkennyarchaeologicalsociety.ie/gravestoneinscriptions.htm
  List of holdings of Kilkenny Archaeological Society

- Gravestone Inscriptions
  scripts.ireland.com/ancestor/browse/counties/leinster/Kilkenny5.htm
  List of published transcripts for Co. Kilkenny

Bennettsbridge
- Bennettsbridge Cemetery, Bennettsbridge, County Kilkenny, Ireland
  www.interment.net/data/ireland/kilkenny/ben__bridge

Celbridge
- Celbridge Gravestones
  www.from-ireland.net/celbridge
  Photographs

Clara
- Clara Churchyard Cemetery, Clara, County Kilkenny, Ireland
  www.interment.net/data/ireland/kilkenny/clara/clara.htm

Dysart
- Dysart Cemetery
  www.findagrave.com
  Click on 'search for a cemetery', search for 'Ireland', & scroll down to 'Dysart'.

Freshford
- Clontubrid Cemetery, Freshford, County Kilkenny, Ireland
  www.interment.net/data/ireland/kilkenny/clontubrid

Kilcullen
- Old Kilcullen Graveyard, County Kildare, Ireland
  www.interment.net/data/ireland/Kildare/Kilcullen

Kilkenny
- Saint John Churchyard, Kilkenny City, County Kilkenny, Ireland
  www.interment.net/data/ireland/kilkenny/stjohn/

- Saint Kieran's Cemetery, County Kilkenny, Ireland
  www.interment.net/data/ireland/kilkenny/st__kierans/kieran.htm
  In Kilkenny

Lisdowney
- County Kilkenny & Laois (Queen's Leix) Graveyards, Ireland:
  Lisdowney
  www.from-ireland.net/graves/kilk/lisdowney.htm

Paulstown
- Paulstown New Cemetery, County Kilkenny, Ireland
  www.interment.net/data/ireland/kilkenny/paulstown/paulstown.htm

Thomastown
- Saint Mary New Cemetery, Thomastown, County Kilkenny, Ireland
  www.interment.net/data/ireland/kilkenny/stmary/stmary.htm

- Thomastown Old Graveyard, County Kilkenny, Ireland
  www.interment.net/data/ireland/kilkenny/thomas__old

Tullaherin
- Tullaherin Cemetery, Tullaherin, County Kilkenny, Ireland
  www.interment.net/data/ireland/kilkenny/tullaherin/tullaherin.htm

Laois

- Ancient Graveyards and Burial Places in Co. Laois
  www.rootsweb.com/~irlcar2/Killeshin__index.htm
  List

- Gravestone Inscriptions, Co. Laois
  www.brennan-laois.com/inscriptions.htm
  Collection of pages

Abbey Leix
- County Laois Graveyards: Abbey Leix, Church of Ireland: Name Index
  www.from-ireland.net/graves/laois/abbeyleixcoi.htm

Aghaboe
- County Laois Graveyards, Ireland: Aghaboe
  www.from-ireland.net/graves/laois/aghaboe.htm

Aharney
- County Laois Graveyards, Ireland: Aharney: Name Index
  www.from-ireland.net/graves/laois/aharney.htm

Arles
- Gravestone Inscriptions: Arles
  www.brennan-laois.com/headstone__index.htm

Attanagh
- County Laois (Leix, Queen's) Ireland: Graveyards: Attanagh: Name Index
  www.from-ireland.net/graves/laois/attanagh.htm

Aughmacart
- County Laois Graveyards: Aughmacart: Name Index
  www.from-ireland.net/graves/laois/aughmacart.htm

Ballyadding
- County Laois Graveyards: Ballyadding: Name Index
  www.from-ireland.net/graves/laois/ballyadding.htm

Ballylynan
- County Laois Graveyards: Ballylynam: Name Index
  www.from-ireland.net/graves/laois/ballylynam.htm

- Gravestone Inscriptions, Ballylynan
  www.brennan-laois.com/headstones__ballylyana__index.htm

Ballyroan
- County Laois Graveyards: Ballyroan: Name Index
  www.from-ireland.net/graves/laois/ballyroan.htm

Bawnhill
- County Laois Graveyards: Bawnhill: Name and Year Index - partial
  www.from-ireland.net/graves/laois/bawnhill.htm

Bordwell
- County Laois Graveyards: Bordwell: Name Index
  www.from-ireland.net/graves/laois/bordwell.htm

Camross
- County Laois Graveyards: Camross: Name Index
  www.from-ireland.net/graves/laois/camross.htm

Clough
- County Laois Graveyards: Clough: Name Index
  www.from-ireland.net/graves/laois/clough.htm

Coolkerry
- County Laois Graveyards: Coolkerry: Name Index
  www.from-ireland.net/graves/laois/coolkerry.htm

Dysart
- Memorials of the Dead: Dysart (Enos) Churchyard
  www.rootsweb.com/~irllex/memorials.htm

Errill
- County Laois Graveyards: Errill: Name Index
  www.from-ireland.net/graves/laois/errill.htm

Killeen
- Gravestones Inscriptions, Killeen
  www.brennan-laois.com/headstones__killeen__index.htm

Killeshin
- Gravestone Inscriptions, Killeshin
  www.brennan-laois.com/headstones__killeshin__index.htm

Killinard
- Memorials of the Dead: Killinard Churchyard
  www.rootsweb.com/~irllex/memorials2.htm

Rahanavannagh
- County Laois Graveyards: Rahanavannagh: Name Index
  www.from-ireland.net/graves/laois/rahanavan.htm

Raheen
- County Laois Graveyards: Raheen: Name Index
  www.from-ireland.net/graves/laois/raheen.htm

Rathsaran
- Rathsaran/Rathsarne Civil Parish Memorial Inscriptions, Eglish,
  Church of Ireland
  www.from-ireland.net/graves/rathsarantrans.htm

Rock of Dunamaise
- Holy Trinity Churchyard, Rock of Dunamaise, County Laois, Ireland
  www.interment.net/data/ireland/laois/holytrinity

Stradbally
- Oak Vale Cemetery, Stradbally, County Laois, Ireland
  www.interment.net/data/ireland/laois/oakvale

- Saint Patrick Churchyard, Stradbally, County Laois, Ireland
  www.interment.net/ireland/laois/patrick

Leitrim

Carrowcrin
- Carrowcrin
  homepage.eircom.net/~kevm/Co.%20Leitrim/Dromahair/
                                Carrowcrin/Carrowcrin.htm
  Index

Conwal Glenade
- Conwal Glenade
  homepage.eircom.net/~kevm/Co.%20Leitrim/
                                Conwal%20Glenade/conwal.htm
  Index

Diffreen
See Glencar

Glencar
- Glencar
  homepage.eircom.net/~kevm/Co.%20Leitrim/Glencar/Glencar.htm
  Index to Diffreen and Killenora Cemeteries inscriptions

Killenora
See Glencar

Kinlough
- Kinlough Graveyard, Kinlough, County Leitrim, Ireland
  www.interment.net/data/ireland/leitrim/kinlough.htm

Limerick
- Limerick Gravestones Inscriptions
  scripts.ireland.com/ancestor/browse/counties/munster/limerick5.htm
  List of published transcripts

Cappamore
- Cappamore, Tower Hill Cemetery
  www.countylimerickgenealogy.com/Cappamore/
                                cappamore__tombstones.htm

Doon
- Doon Cemetery Headstones
  www.countylimerickgenealogy.com/Doon/index.htm

Kilbeheny
- Monumental Inscriptions from the Civil Parish of Kilbeheny
  home.att.net/~wexlababe/monumental__inscriptions__kilbeheny.htm

Mount St. Lawrence
- Mount St. Lawrence Cemetery Records, Limerick, Ireland
  home.att.net/%7Ewexlababe/mt__st__lawrence__cemetery.htm

Oola
- Oola Graveyard Inscriptions
  www.countylimerickgenealogy.com/content/OolaGraveyard.htm

Rathkeale

- Limerick County, Ireland: Rathkeale Roman Catholic Graveyard
  www.from-ireland.net/graves/lim/rathkealerc.htm

- Rathkeale Graveyard, Co, Limerick
  www.celticcousins.net/ireland/cemlim.htm

Londonderry

- Cemetery Inscriptions
  www.rootsweb.com/~nirldy2/Records/church/derrycems.html
  List of transcripts for Londonderry

- Cemetery Inscriptions
  www.rootsweb.com/~nirldy/derrycems.html
  List of transcripts and locations

- Derry Gravestone Inscriptions
  scripts.ireland.com/ancestor/browse/counties/ulster/derry5.htm
  List of transcripts

- County Derry Cemetery Project
  www.rootsweb.com/~nirldy2/cemindex.htm
  19 cemeteries; 'under construction'

- County Derry (Londonderry) Cemetery Inscriptions
  www.rootsweb.com/~nirldy2/Old__Derry/cemetery.htm
  List of transcripts

- County Derry (Londonderry) Cemetery Inscriptions
  www.rootsweb.com/~fianna/county/derry/ldytomb.html

Draperstown

- Saint Patrick Cemetery, County Derry, Northern Ireland
  www.interment.net/data/nire/derry/stpat/patrick.htm

Glendermot

See Tipperary. Dovea

Londonderry

- Derry City Cemetery
  www.findagrave.com
  Click on 'search for a cemetery', search for 'Ireland', scroll down to
  'Derry'.

Moyletra Toy

- Moyletra Toy Parish Church Graveyard
  www.4qd.org/bann/church/des-Moyletra-par-grave.html

Saint Patrick

- Saint Patrick Cemetery, County Derry, Northern Ireland
  www.interment.net/data/nire/derry/stpat/patrick.htm

- Saint Patrick Cemetery located near Sixtowns and Draperstown
  www.rootsweb.com/~nirldy2/St.__Patrick__Cem.htm

Swatragh

- Swatragh Churches of Ireland Record
  www.4qd.org/bann/church/Swatragh/index.html
  Graveyard inscriptions for the Church of Ireland and the Presbyterian
  Church

Longford

- County Longford Headstone Photos
  www.rootsweb.com/~irllog/tombstones/headstones.htm

Ardagh

- Saint Patrick Churchyard, Ardagh, County Longford, Ireland
  www.interment.net/data/ireland/longford/stpat

- Saint Patrick Churchyard
  www.findagrave.com
  Click on 'Search for a cemetery', search 'Ireland', and scroll down to
  'Saint Patrick'. At Ardagh, Co. Longford

Aughafin

- Aughafin Cemetery
  www.mostrim.org/Scrapbook/Introduction.htm
  Co. Longford

Drumlish

- Drumlish Old Cemetery, County Longford, Ireland
  www.interment.net/data/ireland/longford/drumlish/old.htm

Edgeworthstown

- St. John's Graveyard
  www.mostrim.org/Scrapbook/Introduction.htm
  At Edgeworthstown, Co. Longford

Newtownbond
- Newtownbond Church and Graveyard
  www.geocities.com/grymorgan

Louth
- Louth Gravestone Inscriptions
  scripts.ireland.com/ancestor/browse/counties/leinster/louth5.htm
  List of published transcripts

- County Louth Memorial Inscriptions
  www.jbhall.freeservers.com/memorial__inscriptions.htm
  Bibliography

- Name Index to some County Louth Tombstone Inscriptions
  www.jbhall.freeservers.com/index__to__louth__inscriptions.htm

Ardee
- Monumental Inscriptions at old Saint Mary's, Ardee, Co. Louth
  www.from-ireland.net/graves/stmarysardeelouth.htm

Ballymakenny
- Gravestone Inscriptions in Ballymakenny, Co. Lough
  www.from-ireland.net/graves/ballymakennylouth.htm

Calvary
- Calvary Cemetery, County Louth, Ireland
  www.interment.net/data/ireland/louth/calvary
  Near Drogheda

Collon
- Collon Old Cemetery, County Louth, Ireland
  www.interment.net/data/ireland/Louth/collon/oldcollon.htm

Termonfeckin
- Monumental Inscriptions, Termonfeckin Cemetery, Co. Lough
  www.from-ireland.net/graves/termonlouth.htm

Mayo
- Extracts from Inscriptions in Westport - Castlebar area
  freepages.genealogy.rootsweb.com/~deesegenes/cem.html

Achill Island
- Kildownet Old Cemetery, Achill
  freepages.genealogy.rootsweb.com/~deesegenes/kildownet.html

- Slievemore Cemetery, Achill, Co. Mayo
  www.bernieworld.net/Cemeteries/Slievemore/
  Slievemore%20Cemetery.htm

- Sleivemore Old Cemetery, Achill Island, County Mayo, Ireland
  www.interment.net/data/ireland/mayo/sleivemore/sleivemore.htm

Aghamore
- Aghamore Cemetery
  www.findagrave.com
  Click on 'Search for a cemetery', search for 'Ireland', and click on
  'Aghamore'

Aughagower
- Aughagower Cemetery
  freepages.genealogy.rootsweb.com/~deesegenes/gower.htm

Aughavale
- Aughavale Cemetery, Westport, County Mayo, Ireland
  www.bernieworld.net/Cemeteries/Aughavale/
  Aughavale%20Cemetery.htm

Ballaghaderreen
- Kilcolman Old Cemetery, Ballaghaderreen, County Mayo, Ireland
  www.interment.net/data/ireland/mayo/kilcolman/oldkilman.htm

Ballina
- Kilfian Old Graveyard, Ballina, County Mayo, Ireland
  www.interment.net/data/ireland/mayo/kilfian__old

Ballindine
- New Cemetery, Ballindine, County Mayo, Ireland
  www.interment.net/data/ireland/mayo/newcem/new.htm

- Saint Joseph Churchyard Cemetery, Ballindine, County Mayo, Ireland
  www.interment.net/data/ireland/mayo/stjoe

Ballintober
- Ballintober Abbey Cemetery
  freepages.genealogy.rootsweb.com/~deesegenes/tubber.htm

Ballinvilla
- Ballinvilla Graveyard, County Mayo, Ireland
  www.interment.net/data/ireland/mayo/ballinvilla/ballinvilla.htm
- Ballyhean Cemetery
  freepages.genealogy.rootsweb.com/~deesegenes/ballyhean.htm

Bekan
- Bekan Cemetery, Bekan Village, County Mayo, Ireland
  www.interment.net/data/ireland/mayo/bekan/bekan.htm

Bohola
- Bohola Cemetery, County Mayo, Ireland
  www.interment.net/data/ireland/mayo/bohola/

Burriscarra
- Burriscarra Cemetery
  freepages.genealogy.rootsweb.com/~deesegenes/
                                burriscarracemetery.html

Burrishoole
See also Newport
- Burrishoole Cemetery
  www.geocities.com/Heartland/Park/7461/graves.html/
- Burrishoole Cemetery
  freepages.genealogy.rootsweb.com/~deesegenes/burnew.htm

Charlestown
- Charlestown
  homepage.eircom.net/%7Ekevm/Charlestown/Name__index.htm
- Bushfield Church, Charlestown, Co. Mayo
  homepage.eircom.net/%7Ekevm/Bushfield/bushfield__church.htm

Claremorris
- Saint Mary's Abbey Cemetery, Ballinasmala, Claremorris, County Mayo, Ireland
  www.interment.net/data/ireland/mayo/stmary/

- Saint Colman's Cemetery, Claremorris, County Mayo, Ireland
  www.interment.net/data/ireland/mayo/coleman/stcolman.htm
- Tulrahan Cemetery, Claremorris, County Mayo, Ireland
  www.interment.net/data/ireland/mayo/tulrahan.htm

Cong
- Abbey Cemetery, Cong, County Mayo, Ireland
  www.interment.net/data/ireland/mayo/cong

Drum
- Drum Cemetery
  freepages.genealogy.rootsweb.com/~deesegenes/drumcemetery.htm

Gloshpatrick
- Gloshpatrick Cemetery
  freepages.genealogy.rootsweb.com/~deesegenes/glos.htm

Islandeady
- Islandeady Cemetery
  freepages.genealogy.rootsweb.com/~deesegenes/islandeady.html

Kilgeever
- Kilgeever Cemetery
  freepages.genealogy.rootsweb.com/~deesegenes/geev.htm

Killawalla
- Killawalla Cemetery, Co. Mayo
  freepages.genealogy.rootsweb.com/~deesegenes/Killawalla.htm

Kildownet
See Achill

Killeen
See Newport

Kilmeena
See Westport

Kilmovee
- Kilmovee
  homepage.eircom.net/%7Ekevm/Kilmovee/Kilmovee.htm

- Kilmovee Stained Glass Windows
  homepage.eircom.net/%7Ekevm/Co.%20Sligo/Kilmovee/
                                        Kilmovee.htm
  Inscriptions

Kiltimagh
- Kilkinure Cemetery, Kiltimagh, County Mayo, Ireland
  www.interment.net/data/ireland/mayo/kilkinure/kilkinure.htm

Mayo Abbey
- Mayo Abbey
  freepages.genealogy.rootsweb.com/~deesegenes/mayoab.htm

Meelick
- Meelick New Cemetery
  homepage.eircom.net/%7Ekevm/Meelick/New.htm
  List of inscriptions

- Meelick Old Cemetery
  homepage.eircom.net%7Ekevm/Meelick/Old.htm
  List of inscriptions

Murrisk
- Gravestone Inscriptions, Murrisk, Co. Mayo
  myhome.ispdr.net.au/~mgrogan/cork/murrisk.htm

- Murrisk Cemetery
  www.bernieworld.net/cemeteries/Murrisk/Murrisk%20Cemetery.htm

- Murrisk Abbey Cemetery
  freepages.genealogy.rootsweb.com/~deesegenes/murr.htm

Newport
- Burrishoole Cemetery, Newport, Co. Mayo
  www.bernieworld.net/Cemeteries/Burrishoole/
                                 Burrishoole%20Cemetery.htm

- Killeen Cemetery, Newport County Mayo, Ireland
  www.bernieworld.net/Cemeteries/Killeen/Killeen%20Cemetery.htm

Rathbane
- Rathbane Cemetery
  freepages.genealogy.rootsweb.com/~deesegenes/
                                 rathbanecemetery.html

Straide
- Straide Cemetery, County Mayo
  freepages.genealogy.rootsweb.com/~deesegenes/straide.htm

Swinford
- Midfield Cemetery, Swinford, County Mayo, Ireland
  www.interment.net/data/ireland/mayo/midfield

Turlough
- Turlough Cemetery
  freepages.genealogy.rootsweb.com/~deesegenes/turlough.htm

Westport
- Kilmeena Cemetery, Westport, County Mayo
  www.bernieworld.net/cemeteries/Kilmeena/
                                 Kilmeena%20Cemetery.htm

Meath
- Meath Gravestone Inscriptions
  scripts.ireland.com/ancestor/browse/counties/leinster/meath5.htm
  List of transcripts

Ardcath
- Ardcath Cemetery, Ardcath, County Meath, Ireland
  www.interment.net/data/ireland/meath/ardcath

Ashbourne
- Immaculate Conception Churchyard, Ashbourne, County Meath, Ireland
  www.interment.net/data/ireland/meath/immaculate/conception.htm

- Greenogue Cemetery, Donaghmore, Ashbourne, County Meath, Ireland
  www.interment.net/data/ireland/meath/greenogue/greenogue.htm

- Killegland Cemetery, Ashbourne, County Meath, Ireland
  www.interment.net/data/ireland/meath/killegland

Athboy
- County Meath Graveyards: Athboy: Name Index
  www.from-ireland.net/graves/meath/athboy.htm

Ballinlough
- Ballinlough Churchyard, Ballinlough, County Meath, Ireland
  www.interment.net/data/ireland/meath/ballinlough

Balrath
- Ballymagarvey Cemetery, Balrath, County Meath, Ireland
  www.interment.net/data/ireland/meath/ballymagarvey

Batterstown
- Batterstown Churchyard Cemetery, Batterstown, County Meath, Ireland
  www.interment.net/data/ireland/meath/batterstown/balterstown.htm

Castletown
- Free Genealogy Death Records on Graves in the Courtown Road Cemetery, Castletown, Co. Wexford, Ireland
  ancestorsatrest.com/cemetery__records/
                    castletown__courtown__road__cemetery__ireland.shtml

Clonalvy
- Clonalvy Cemetery, Clonalvy, County Meath, Ireland
  www.interment.net/data/ireland/meath/clonalvy/clonalvy.htm

Crossmacole
See Cushinstown

Curraha
- Saint Andrew Cemetery, Curraha, County Meath, Ireland
  www.interment.net/data/ireland/meath/standy

Cushinstown
- Crossmacole Cemetery, Cushinstown, County Meath, Ireland
  www.interment.net/data/ireland/meath/crossmacole

Duleek
- Some Monumental Inscriptions from Duleek Church of Ireland, Co. Meath
  www.from-ireland.net/graves/duleekchurchlanemeath.htm

Dunboyne
- County Meath Graveyards: Dunboyne, Church of Ireland Gravestones: Name Index
  www.from-ireland.net/graves/meath/dunboyne.htm

Dunderry
- Dunderry Cemetery, Dunderry, County Meath, Ireland
  www.interment.net/data/ireland/meath/dunderry

- Retaine Cemetery, Dunderry, County Meath, Ireland
  www.interment.net/data/ireland/meath/retaine

Dunsany
See Tara

Dunshaughlin
- Dunshaughlin Cemetery, Dunshaughlin, County Meath, Ireland
  www.interment.net/data/ireland/meath/dunshaughlin/
                              dunshaughlin.htm

Kells
- Some Monumental Inscriptions from Kells, Co. Meath
  www.from-ireland.net/graves/kellsmeath.htm

Kentstown
- Kentstown Churchyard Cemetery, Kentstown, County Meath
  www.interment.net/data/ireland/meath/kentstown/kents.htm

Killegland
See Ashbourne

Kilmessen
- Church of the Nativity Cemetery, Kilmessan, County Meath, Ireland
  www.interment.net/data/ireland/meath/church__nativity

Loughcrew
- List of Surnames in Loughcrew Graveyard, Co. Meath
  ancestorsatrest.com/cemetery__records/
                    loughcrew__cemetery__county__meath.shtml

Moy
- County Meath Graveyards: Moy, near Summerhill: Name Index
  www.from-ireland.net/graves/meath/moy.htm

Moyagher
- County Meath Graves: Moyagher: Name Index
  www.from-ireland.net/graves/meath/moyagher.htm

Moynalty
- Saint Mary Cemetery, Moynalty, County Meath, Ireland
  www.interment.net/data/ireland/meath/moynalty/moynalty.htm

Navan
- Saint Mary Cemetery, Navan, County Meath, Ireland
  www.interment.net/data/ireland/meath/stmary__navan

Oldcastle
- Saint Keverne of Cemetery, Oldcastle, County Meath, Ireland
  www.interment.net/data/ireland/meath/loughcrew/loughcrew.htm

- Saint Oliver Plunkett Churchyard, Oldcastle, County Meath, Ireland
  www.interment.net/data/ireland/meath/plunkett/stoliver.htm

- Saint Bridget Cemetery, Oldcastle, County Meath, Ireland
  www.interment.net/data/ireland/meath/stbridget/bridget.htm

Rathcore
- Rathcore Church of Ireland, Co. Meath: Church and Graveyard Inscriptions
  homepage.eircom.net/~Rathmolyongraveyard/directory/HOMER.html

Rathfeigh
See Tara

Rathmolyon
- Rathmolyon Graveyard Inscriptions
  homepage.eircom.net/~Rathmolyongraveyard/directory/Home.html

Ratoath
- Ratoath Cemetery, Ratoath, County Meath, Ireland
  www.interment.net/data/ireland/meath/ratoath

Retaine
See Dunderry

Skryne
See Tara

Tara
- Saint Columcille Churchyard, Skryne, Tara, County Meath, Ireland
  www.interment.net/data/ireland/meath/columcille

- Immaculate Conception Churchyard, Rathfeigh, Tara, County Meath, Ireland
  www.interment.net/data/ireland/meath/immaculate__rath

- Church of the Assumption Churchyard, Dunsany, Tara, County Meath, Ireland
  www.interment.net/data/ireland/meath/assumption

Monaghan
- Monaghan Gravestone Inscriptions
  scripts.ireland.com/ancestor/browse/counties/ulster/monaghan5.htm
  List of published transcripts

Clones
- Clones Round Tower Graveyard, Clones, Co. Monaghan
  www.from-ireland.net/graves/clonesroundtower.htm
  Monumental Inscriptions

Offaly

Durrow
- Saint Colmcille Churchyard, Durrow, County Offaly, Ireland
  www.interment.net/data/ireland/offaly/colmcille

Lusmagh
- Kilmachonna, Lusmagh: Offaly Tombstone Inscriptions
  www.from-ireland.net/graves/kilmachonnaoffaly.htm

Roscommon
- Gravestone Inscriptions
  scripts.ireland.com/ancestor/browse/counties/
  connacht/roscomm5.htm

  List of transcripts for Co. Roscommon

Athlone
- Drum Cemetery, Athlone, County Roscommon, Ireland
  www.rootsweb.com/~irish/igsi__published/cemetery/roscdrum.htm
  General discussion; no inscriptions

Baslic
- Baslic Cemetery
  homepage.eircom.net/~kevm/Baslic/Baslic__2.htm

Boyle

- Assylinn Cemetery, Boyle, County Roscommon, Ireland
  www.interment.net/data/ireland/roscommon/assylinn/assylinn.htm

- Estersnow Cemetery, Croghan, Boyle, County Roscommon, Ireland
  www.interment.net/data/ireland/roscommon/estersnow/
  estersnow.htm

- Kilnamanagh Cemetery, Boyle, County Roscommon, Ireland
  www.interment.net/data/ireland/roscommon/kilnamanagh/
  kilnamanagh.htm

Elphin

- Saint Patrick Churchyard Cemetery, Elphin Town, County Roscommon, Ireland
  www.interment.net/data/ireland/roscommon/stpat/stpat.htm

- Kiltrustan Cemetery, Elphin, County Roscommon, Ireland
  www.interment.net/data/ireland/roscommon/kiltrustan/
  kiltrustan.htm

Kilglass

- Kilglass Cemetery, Kilglass, County Roscommon, Ireland
  www.interment.net/data/ireland/roscommon/kilglass/kilglass.htm

Shankill

- Old Shankill Cemetery, Shankill, County Roscommon, Ireland
  www.interment.net/data/ireland/roscommon/
  oldshankhill/shankill.htm

Strokestown

- Strokestown Cemetery, Stokestown, County Roscommon, Ireland
  www.interment.net/data/ireland/roscommon/stokestown/stoke.htm

Tulsk

- Tulsk Cemetery, Tulsk Village, County Roscommon, Ireland
  www.interment.net/data/ireland/roscommon/tulsk/tulsk.htm

- Kilcooley Cemetery, Kilcooley, Tulsk, County Roscommon, Ireland
  www.interment.net/data/ireland/roscommon/kilcooley/kilcooley.htm

Sligo

- Burial in Sligo County, Ireland
  www.rootsweb.com/~irlsli/burialopen.html
  Monumental inscriptions for many cemeteries

Ahamlish

- Ahamlish
  homepage.eircom.net/~Kevm/Co.%20Sligo/Ahamlish/Ahamlish.htm

Ballintogher

- Killery: Ballintogher Church, Co. Sligo
  homepage.eircom.net/~kevm/Co.%20Sligo/
  Ballintogher/Ballintogher.htm

Ballisodare

- Old Ballisodare Cemetery, County Sligo, Ireland
  www.interment.net/data/ireland/sligo/ballisadare/ballisadare.htm

Ballygawley

- Ballygawley
  homepage.eircom.net/~kevm/Co.%20Sligo/
  Ballygawley/Ballygawley.htm

  List of inscriptions at Kilross Cemetery

Ballymote

- Saint Columbas Cemetery, County Sligo, Ireland
  www.interment.net/data/ireland/sligo/stcolumbas.htm
  In Ballymote

Banada Abbey

- Banada Abbey
  homepage.eircom.net/~kevm/Co.%20Sligo/
  Banada/Banada__Abby.htm

  Monumental inscriptions

Boyle

- Killaraght Cemetery, Boyle, County Sligo, Ireland
  www.interment.net/data/ireland/sligo/killaraght/killaraght.htm

Calry

- Calry
  www.eircom.net/~kevm/Co.%20Sligo/Calry/Calry.htm

Carrigans
- Carrigans
  homepage.eircom.net/~kevm/Co.%20Sligo/Carrigans/Carrigans.htm

Carrowanty
- Carrowanty Cemetery, County Sligo, Ireland
  www.interment.net/data/ireland/sligo/carrowanty/carrowanty.htm

Collooney
- Collooney Cemetery, Collooney, County Sligo, Ireland
  www.interment.net/data/ireland/sligo/collooney/collooney.htm

Curry
- Curry
  homepage.eircom.net/~kevm/Co.%20Sligo/
                          Curry/Curry__Church.htm

Drumcliffe
- St. Columba's Church, Drumcliffe, Co. Sligo
  homepage.eircom.net/~kevm/Co.%20Sligo/
                          Drumcliffe/Drumcliffe.htm

Easky
- Roslea Cemetery, Easky
  www.puregolduk.com/bren/mieasky.htm

Gurteen
- Gurteen Cemetery, Gurteen, County Sligo, Ireland
  www.interment.net/data/ireland/sligo/gurteen/gurteen.htm

Keelogues
- Keelogues
  homepage.eircom.net/~kevm/Co.%20Sligo/Keelogues/Keelogues.htm

Killery
See Ballintogher

Kilmacowen
- Kilmacowen
  homepage.eircom.net/~kevm/Co.%20Sligo/
                          kilmacowen/kilmacowen/htm
  List of inscriptions

Lisadell
- Lisadell Church, Co. Sligo
  homepage.eircom.net/kevm/Co.%20Sligo/Lisadell/Lisadell.htm
  Photographs of headstones

Rathcormack
- Rathcormack
  homepage.eircom.net/~kevm/Co.%20Sligo/
                          Rathcormack/Rathcormack.htm
  List of inscriptions

Roslea
See Easky

Rosses Point
- Rosses Point Cemetery
  homepage.eircom.net/~kevm/Co.%20Sligo/Rosses__PointIntro.htm
  List of inscriptions

Scarden
- Scarden
  homepage.eircom.net/~kevm/Co.%20Sligo/Ahamlish/
                          Scarden/Intro.htm
  List of inscriptions

Sooey
- Sooey
  homepage.eircom.net/~kevm/Co.%20Sligo/Sooey/Sooey.htm
  List of inscriptions at Ballinakill Cemetery

- Saint Joseph Cemetery, County Sligo, Ireland
  www.interment.net/data/ireland/sligo/stjoseph/joseph.htm
  In Sooey

Templeboy
- [Templeboy Cemeteries]
  www.puregolduk.com/bren/MI's%20Co.%20Sligo.htm

- Tombstones at Corcagh Cemetery, Templeboy Parish
  www.rootsweb.com/~irlsli/cemetery4.html
  Surnames only

Templeronan
- Templeronan Cemetery, County Sligo, Ireland
  www.interment.net/data/ireland/sligo/templeronan/templeronan.htm

Thurlestrane
- Thurlestrane
  homepage.eircom.net/~kevm/Co.%20Sligo/
  Thurlestrane/thurlestrane.htm
  Inscriptions

Tipperary
- Cemeteries
  www.rootsweb.com/~irltip2/cemeteries__ndx.htm
  Collection of pages for Tipperary, individually listed below

- Tipperary Headstones
  www.rootsweb.com/~irltip2/tombstones/index.htm
  Database with photographs

- Assorted Headstone Extracts
  www.rootsweb.com/~irltip2/cemeteries/misc__stones.htm

- Assorted Tipperary Burials
  www.rootsweb.com/~irltip2/cemeteries/assorted__cems.htm

Ardcrony
- Some Memorials to the Dead: Ardcrony Churchyard
  www.rootsweb.com/~irltip2/memorials.htm

Ardfinnan
See Rochestown

Ballylooby
- Ballylooby
  www.geocities.com/luanndevries/BALLYLOOBY.html

Ballyporeen
- Transcription of Various Headstones from Templetenny Cemetery,
  Ballyporeen Parish, Tipperary
  www.rootsweb.com/~irltip2/cemeteries/templetenny__cem.htm

Bansha
- Bansha: Bansha Parish
  www.geocities.com/luanndevries/Bansha.html
  www.rootsweb.com/~irltip2/cemeteries/cem__bansha.html

Cahir
- Cahir: Old Church
  www.geocities.com/luanndevries/CAHIR.html
  www.rootsweb.com/~irltip2/cem__cahir.htm

Clogheen
- Castlegrace Graveyard, Clogheen, County Tipperary
  www.geocities.com/luanndevries/CASTLEGRACE.html
  www.rootsweb.com/~irltip2/cem__castlegrace.htm

Clonmel
- Marlfield, Clonmel Parish
  www.geocities.com/luanndevries/Marlfield.html
  www.rootsweb.com/~irltip2/cem__marlfield.htm

- Saint Patrick Cemetery, Clonmel, County Tipperary, Ireland
  www.interment.net/data/ireland/tipperary/stpatrick/patrick.htm

Derrygrath
- Derrygrath
  www.geocities.com/luanndevries/DERRYGRATH01.html
  Monumental inscriptions

- Derrygrath
  www.rootsweb.com/~irltip2/cem__derrygrath.htm

Dovea
- Irish Cemeteries: Dovea, Old Glendermott, Ileigh, Inch Old Cemetery
  members.iinet.net.au/~sgrives/cemeteries__irelan__2.htm
  Inscriptions. Old Glendermott is in Londonderry

Emly
- Emly Gravestone Inscriptions
  www.rootsweb.com/~irltip/Records/EmlyGraveyard.htm
  List only

Fethard
- Augustinian Abbey Cemetery, Fethard, County Tipperary, Ireland
  www.interment.net/data/ireland/tipperary/
                              augustinian__abbey/august.htm

Ileigh
See Dovea

Inch
See also Dovea
- Partial list of Tombstones in Inch graveyard
  www.rootsweb.com/~irltip2/cemeteries/inch__cem.htm

Kilcommon
- Kilcommon: Protestant
  www.geocities.com/luanndevries/KILCOMMON-PROT.html
  www.rootsweb.com/~irltip2/cem__kilcommon__prot.htm

- Kilcommon: Quaker
  www.rootsweb.com/~irltip2/cem__kilcommon.htm

Killadriffe
- Killadriffe Headstone Inscriptions (partial)
  www.rootsweb.com/~irltip2/kiladriffe.htm

Killardry
- Some Memorials to the Dead in County Tipperary: Killardry
  Churchyard
  www.rootsweb.com/~irltip2/killardry.htm

Lorrha
- Lorrha Cemetery, County Tipperary, Ireland
  www.interment.net/data/ireland/tipperary/lorrha/

Loughloher
- Loughloher (graveyard and church in ruins)
  www.rootsweb.com/~irltip2/cem__loughloher.htm

Loughmore
- Cemetery Headstone Inscriptions Ireland: Loughmore Catholic Cemetery
  members.webone.com.au/~sgrieves/cemetries%20ireland3.htm

Mortlestown
- Mortlestown
  www.geocities.com/luanndevries/MORTLESTOWN01.html

- Mortlestown
  www.rootsweb.com/~irltip2/cem__mortlestown.htm

Mt. Bruis
- Mt. Bruis Graveyard Inscriptions
  www.rootsweb.com/~irltip/Records/MtBruisGraveyard.htm

Outrath
- Outrath
  www.geocities.com/luanndevries/OUTRATH.html
  Monumental inscriptions

- Outrath
  www.rootsweb.com/~irltip2/cem__outrath.htm

Rochestown
- Rochestown, Ardfinnan
  www.geocities.com/luanndevries/Rochestown.html

- Rochestown - Ardfinnan
  www.rootsweb.com/~irltip2/cem__roches.htm

Roscrea
- Saint Cronan Church of Ireland Churchyard, Roscrea, County
  Tipperary, Ireland
  www.interment.net/data/ireland/tipperary/stcronan/

Shanrahan
- Shanrahan Graveyard
  www.geocities.com/luanndevries/SHANRAHAN.html
  www.rootsweb.com/~irltip2/cem__shanrahan.htm

Shronell
- Shronell Graveyard Inscriptions
  www.rootsweb.com/~irltip/Records/ShronellGraveyard.htm

Solohead
- Solohead Gravestone Inscriptions
  www.rootsweb.com/~irltip/Records/Soloheadgraveyard.htm

Templetenny
See Ballyporeen

Thurles
- Partial Listing of Tombs in St. Mary's Graveyard, Thurles
  www.rootsweb.com/~irltip2/cemeteries/st__marys__thurles.htm

Uskane
- Monumental Inscriptions at Uskane, Co. Tipperary
  www.from-ireland.net/graves/uskanetipperary.htm

Whitechurch
- Whitechurch
  www.geocities.com/luanndevries/WHITECHURCH.html

- Whitechurch
  www.rootsweb.com/~irltip2/cem__whitechurch.htm

Tyrone
- County Tyrone Cemetery Index
  www.rootsweb.com/~nirtyr3/Cemetery/cemetery.html
  Includes inscriptions from various cemeteries

Albany
- Albany Presbyterian, Tyrone
  www.yorick.plus.com/Tyronegraves/Albany/FrameSet.htm

Castlederg
- Roll of Honour, First Castlederg Presbyterian Church 1914-1918
  freepages.genealogy.rootsweb.com/
                   ~cotyroneireland/churchrecord/dergww1.html

Cloger
- Cloger Cemetery
  www.rootsweb.com/~nirtyr3/Cemetery/Gloger/index.htm

- Saint MaCartan's Cathedral and Cemetery
  www.rootsweb.com/~nirtyr3/St.MaCartans/index.htm
  In Cloger. Photographs of gravestones

Clonoe
- Gravestone Inscriptions, Saint Michael's, Clonoe
  www.from-ireland.net/graves/clonoetyrone.htm

Dunmoyle
- Dunmoyle Chapel Graveyard
  www.rootsweb.com/~nirtyr3/Cemetery/Dunmoyle/dunmoyle.htm

Errigle
- Errigle Cross Cemetery
  www.rootsweb.com/~nirtyr3/Cemetery/Errigle/errigle1.htm
  Continued at /errigle2.htm & /errigle3.htm

Glenhoy
- Glenhoy Presbyterian Church
  freepages.genealogy.rootsweb.com/
                   ~cotyroneireland/churchrecord/glenhoy.html

Killeeshil
- Killeeshil Chapel and grounds used by Protestants and Catholics
  www.rootsweb.com/~nirtyr3/Cemetery/Killeeshil/killeeshil.htm

Killeter
See Termonamongan

Killyman
- St. Andrew's, Killyman, Tyrone
  www.yorick.pluscom/Tyronegraves/KillymanParish/FrameSet.htm

Magherakeel
See Termonamongan

Scarvagherin
- Headstone Inscriptions from Scarvagherin Burial Ground near Castlederg
  freepages.genealogy.rootsweb.com/~cotyroneireland/
                   burial/scarvagherin.html

Termonamongan
- Headstone Inscriptions from St. Patrick's Church Burial Ground, Aghyaran, Termonamongan
  freepages.genealogy.rootsweb.com/~cotyroneireland/
                   burial/stpatrick.html

- Headstone Inscriptions from Magherakeel Burial Ground, Killeter. Termonamongan Parish
  freepages.genealogy.rootsweb.com/~cotyroneireland/
                   burial/magherakeel.html

Waterford

- Waterford Gravestone Inscriptions
  scripts.ireland.com/ancestor/browse/counties/munster/waterfd5.htm
  List of published transcripts

- Waterford City and County Headstones
  www.rootsweb.com/~irlwat2/headstones/index.htm
  Database of photographs

Drumcannon
- Tallow Churchyard; Whitechurch Churchyard; Drumcannon
  www.rootsweb.com/~irlwat2/talmem.htm

Dunhill
- Dunhill Churchyard
  www.rootsweb.com/~irlwat2/dunmem.htm

Dunmore East
- Killea Church, Dunmore East, Co. Waterford
  homepage.eircom.net/~kevm/Co.%20Waterford/Killea/Killea.htm
  List of monuments

Kilmacow
- St. Senans Cemetery, Kilmacow
  www.from-ireland.net/graves/senanskilmacowwat.htm
  Inscriptions

Lismore
- Lismore: St. Carthagh's Cathedral
  www.rootsweb.com/~irlwat2/lismmem.htm
  Survey of inscriptions

Westmeath

- Westmeath Gravestone Inscriptions
  scripts.ireland.com/ancestor/browse/counties/leinster/westmth5.htm
  List of transcripts

Athlone
- Cornamagh Cemetery, Athlone, County Westmeath, Ireland
  www.interment.net/data/ireland/westmeath/cornamagh

Castlepollard
- Lickbla Graveyard, Castlepollard, County Westmeath, Ireland
  www.interment.net/data/ireland/westmeath/lickbla

- Killafree Cemetery, Castlepollard, County Westmeath, Ireland
  www.interment.net/data/ireland/westmeath/killafree/killafree.htm

- Saint Michael Cemetery, Castlepollard, County Westmeath, Ireland
  www.interment.net/data/ireland/westmeath/stmike

Cornamagh
See Athlone

Delvin
- Headstones in St. Mary's Churchyard, Delvin, Co. Westmeath
  www.from-ireland.net/graves/delvinwestmeath.htm

Finea
- Castletown Churchyard, Finea, County Westmeath, Ireland
  www.interment.net/data/ireland/westmeath/castletown

Fore
- St. Feichin Churchyard New Cemetery, Fore, County Westmeath, Ireland
  www.interment.net/data/ireland/westmeath/newfechin.htm

- Saint Feichin Old Cemetery, Fore, County Westmeath
  www.interment.net/data/ireland/westmeath/oldfechin/fechins.htm

Lickbla
See Castlepollard

Mullingar
- Turin Cemetery, Mullingar, County Westmeath, Ireland
  www.interment.net/data/ireland/westmeath/turin/turin.htm

Wexford
- Graveyards & Churches in Co. Wexford
  www.from-ireland.net/graves/wexchugraves.htm
  Archaeological description

- Wexford Gravestones: Place Name Index
  www.from-ireland.net/graves/wex/placenames.htm

- New York References in County Wexford Gravestone Inscriptions
  freepages.genealogy.rootsweb.com/~nyirish/
  Memorial%20Inscriptions%20NEW%20YORK%20references.html

Ambrosetown
- Wexford Gravestones: Name Index: Ambrosetown
  www.from-ireland.net/graves/ambrosewex.htm

Ardamine
- Ardamine Graveyard
  www.from-ireland.net/graves/ardaminewexford.htm

Askamore
- Askamore Graveyard, Co. Wexford
  www.from-ireland.net/graves/askamorewexford.htm
  Inscriptions

Ballymagaret
- Wexford Gravestones Name Index: St. Mary's R.C. Church,
  Ballymagaret, Co. Wexford, Ireland
  www.from-ireland.net/graves/wex/bgarrett.htm

Ballymitty
- Wexford Gravestones Name Index: Ballymitty St. Peter's R.C. Church
  www.from-ireland.net/graves/ballymittywexford.htm

Bannow
- Wexford Gravestones Name Index: Bannow
  www.from-ireland.net/graves/bannowwex.htm

Barntown
- Wexford Gravestones Name Index: Barntown
  www.from-ireland.net/graves/barntownwex.htm

Bunclody
- Calvary Cemetery, County Wexford, Ireland
  www.interment.net/data/ireland/wexford/calvary/calvary.htm

- Saint Mary C. of I. Churchyard, Bunclody, County Wexford, Ireland
  www.interment.net/data/ireland/wexford/stmary/

Calvary Cemetery, County Wexford, Ireland
www.interment.net/data/ireland/wexford/calvary/calvary.htm
In Bunclody

Castletown
- St. Patrick's Church, Castletown, Co. Wexford
  ancestorsatrest.com/ireland__genealogy__data/
  st__patricks__church__cemetery__wexford.shtml

Cleristown
- Wexford Gravestones Name Index: Cleriestown (Cleristown)
  St. Mannan's R.C. Church
  www.from-ireland.net/graves/cleriestownwex.htm

- Cleariestown Graveyard in County Wexford
  ancestorsatrest.com/cemetery__records/
  cleriestown__cemetery__county__wexford.shtml

Crosstown
- Saint Ibar Cemetery (Crosstown Cemetery), County Wexford, Ireland
  www.interment.net/data/ireland/wexford/stibar

Donaghmore
- Donaghmore Old Graveyard
  www.from-ireland.net/graves/donaghmoreoldwex.htm

Duncormack
- Free Genealogy Death Records on Gravestones in Duncormack,
  County Wexford, Ireland
  ancestorsatrest.com/cemetery__records/
  duncormack__wexford__ireland.shtml

Ferns
- Free Genealogy Death Records on Graves in the Ferns Cemetery
  County Wexford, Ireland
  ancestorsatrest.com/cemetery__records/
  ferns__cemetery__county__wexford.shtml

Gorey
- Saint Michael Cemetery, Gorey, County Wexford, Ireland
  www.interment.net/data/ireland/wexford/stmike

Hook
- Hook Church Cemetery, County Wexford, Ireland
www.interment.net/data/ireland/wexford/hook/hook.htm

Kilcavan
- Wexford Gravestones Name Index: Kilcavan
www.from-ireland.net/graves/kilcavan.htm

Kilgarvan
- Kilgarvan Graveyard
freepages.genealogy.rootsweb.com/~nyirish/
Graveyard%20Inscriptions.html

Kilgorman
- Wexford Gravestones Name Index: Kilgorman
www.from-ireland.net/graves/wex/kilgorman.htm

Kilmannon
- Free Genealogy Death Records on Gravestones in Kilmannon in County Wexford
ancestersatrest.com/cemetery__records/
kilmannon__county__%20wexford.shtml

Kilmore
- Grange Cemetery, Kilmore, County Wexford, Ireland
www.interment.net/data/ireland/wexford/oldgrange/grange.htm

Kilmyshall
- Wexford Gravestones Name Index: Kilmyshall, Old
www.from-ireland.net/graves/wex/kilmyshallold.htm

- Wexford Gravestones Name Index: Kilmyshall R.C.
www.from-ireland.net/graves/wex/Kilmyshallrc.htm

Kilnahue
- Wexford Gravestones: Kilnahue old (near Gorey), Wexford, Ireland
www.from-ireland.net/graves/wex/kilnahueold.htm
Name index

Kilrush
- Wexford Gravestones Name Index: Kilrush, Church of Ireland Graveyard, Co. Wexford, Ireland
www.from-ireland.net/graves/wex/kilrushcoi.htm
Name index

- Wexford Gravestones Name Index: Kilrush Roman Catholic, Ireland
www.from-ireland.net/graves/wex/kilrushc.htm

- Kilrush R.C.
www.from-ireland.net/graves/kilrushwexford.htm
List of surnames from inscriptions

Kiltennel
- Kiltennel Graveyard, St. Sinchell, Church of Ireland
www.from-ireland.net/graves/kiltennellwexford.htm

Knockbrandon
- Wexford Gravestones Name Index: Knockbrandon Old, Wexford, Ireland
www.from-ireland.net/graves/wex/knockbrandonld.htm

Leskinfere
- Wexford Gravestones Name Index: Leskinfere, St. Lukes Church of Ireland, Ireland
www.from-ireland.net/graves/wex/leskinfere.htm

Monaseed
- Wexford Gravestones Name Index: Monaseed Roman Catholic Graveyard, Ireland
www.from-ireland.net/graves/wex/monaseedrc.htm

Prospect
- Wexford Gravestones Name Index: Prospect Church of Ireland Graveyard, Ireland
www.from-ireland.net/graves/wex/prospectcoi.htm

- Prospect Grave Yard
www.findagrave.com
Click on 'Search for a cemetery', search 'Ireland', and scroll down to 'Prospect'

Rathangan
- Surname Index, Rathangan New Graveyard, County Wexford, Ireland
ancestorsatrest.com/cemetery__records/
rathangan__new__graveyard.shtml

- Surname Index Rathangan Old Graveyard, County Wexford, Ireland
ancestorsatrest.com/cemetery__records/
rathangan__old__graveyard.shtml

Taghmon
- Wexford Gravestones Name Index: St. Manna's, Taghmon, Wexford, Ireland
  www.from-ireland.net/graves/wex/taghmannas.htm

Templeshanbo
- Templeshanbo Old
  www.from-ireland.net/graves/templeshwex.htm
  Some inscriptions, with list of surnames from others

Templetown
- Templetown Cemetery, County Wexford, Ireland
  www.interment.net/data/ireland/wexford/templeton/temple.htm

Wicklow
- Search County Wicklow Graveyards for your Ancestors
  www.rootsweb.com/~irlwic2/grave-yards
  Collection of inscriptions from various places, some separately listed below

Arklow
- County Wicklow, Arklow Parish: St. Gabriel's, Arklow, Barinsky Gravestone Inscriptions (or death records)
  www.cmcrp.net/Wicklow/stgabcem.htm
- St. Mary's, Arklow Graveyard in Wicklow County, Ireland
  **www.rootsweb.com/~irlwic2/grave__yards/
  St__Marys__Arklow__Graveyard.htm**

Ashford
- Wicklow Gravestones Name Index: Church of the Holy Rosary, Ashford, Co. Wicklow
  www.from-ireland.net/graves/wicklow/holyrosaryashford.htm
  Brief

Avoca
- Index for Avoca Old Graveyard
  **www.rootsweb.com/~irlwic2/grave__yards/
  avoca__old__graveyard.htm**

Ballinatone
- Ballinatone Church of Ireland, Co. Wicklow
  **www.rootsweb.com/~irlwic2/grave__yards/
  ballimatone__graveyard.htm**

Baltinglass
- Baltinglass Cemetery, County Wicklow, Ireland
  www.interment.net/data/ireland/wicklow/baltinglass/baltinglass.htm
- Saint Mary Abbey Churchyard, Baltinglass, County Wicklow, Ireland
  www.interment.net/data/ireland/wicklow/stmary/

Barranisky
- Free Genealogy Death Records on Headstones in the Barranisky Cemetery, County Wicklow, Ireland
  **www.ancestorsatrest.com/cemetery__records/
  barranisky__cemetery__county__wicklow__ireland.shtml**

Bray
- Wicklow Gravestones Name Index: Church of the Most Holy Redeemer, Bray, Co. Wicklow
  www.from-ireland.net/graves/wicklow/holyredeembray.htm
- Wicklow Gravestones Name Index: Bray Little Graveyard (St. Peter's Chapel)
  www.from-ireland.net/graves/wicklow/littlebray.htm

Conary
- St. Bartholomew's Church Graveyard, Conary Townland, Co. Wicklow, Ireland
  **www.rootsweb.com/~irlwic2/grave__yards/
  conary__parish__graveyard.htm**

Davistown
- Davistown Cemetery, Davistown, County Wicklow, Ireland
  www.interment.net/data/ireland/wicklow/davistown/davis.htm

Delgany
- Wicklow Gravestones Name Index: Delgany, old
  www.from-ireland.net/graves/wicklow/delganyold.htm

Derralossary
- Wicklow Gravestones Name Index: Derralossary
  www.from-ireland.net/graves/wicklow/derralossary.htm

Dunlavin
- Dunlavin Cemetery, Dunlavin, County Wicklow, Ireland
  www.interment.net/data/ireland/wicklow/dunlavin/dunlavin.htm

- Saint Nicholas C of I Churchyard, Dunlavin, County Wicklow, Ireland
  www.interment.net/data/ireland/wicklow/stnick

- Saint Nicholas Cemetery, County Wicklow, Ireland
  www.interment.net/data/ireland/wicklow/nicholas/nicholas.htm
  At Tournant, Dunlavin

Ennisboyne
- Index for Ennisboyne, 3 Miles Water
  www.ancestorsatrest.com/cemeteryrecords/
                          ennisboyne__3__mile__water.shtml

Glendalough
- Glendalough Seven Churches, County Wicklow, Ireland
  www.ancestorsatrest.com/cemetery__records/
                          glendalough__seven__churches.shtml

- Saint Kevin Cemetery, Glendalough, County Wicklow, Ireland
  www.interment.net/data/ireland/wicklow/stkev__glen/

Glentree
- Glentree German War Cemetery
  www.findagrave.com
  Click on 'search for a cemetery', search for 'Ireland', and scroll down to
  'Glentree'

Greenane
- Free Genealogy Death Records on Headstones in the St. Columbus
  Church Cemetery, Greenane, County Wicklow, Ireland
  www.ancestorsatrest.com/cemetery__records/
          st__columbus__church__cemetery__greenane__wicklow.shtml

Heighington
- Heighington Burial Ground, County Wicklow, Ireland
  www.interment.net/data/ireland/wicklow/
                          heighington/heighington.htm

Hollywood
- Free Genealogy Death Records on Headstones in the Hollywood Church
  of Ireland Cemetery, County Wicklow, Ireland
  ancestorsatrest.com/cemetery__records/
                  hollywood__cemetery__wicklow.shtml

- Free Genealogy Death Records on Headstones in the St. Kevins Roman
  Catholic Church Cemetery, Hollywood, County Wicklow, Ireland
  ancestorsatrest.com/cemetery__records/
                  st__kevins__church__cemetery__wicklow.shtml

Killoughter
- Wicklow Gravestones Name Index: Killoughter
  www.from-ireland.net/graves/wicklow/killoughter.htm

Kilmacanogue
- Wicklow Gravestones Name Index: Kilmacanogue.htm
  www.from-ireland.net/graves/wicklow/kilmacanogue.htm

Kilquade
- Wicklow Gravestones Name Index: Kilquade
  www.from-ireland.net/graves/wicklow/kilquade.htm

Kilranalagh
- Kilranalagh Graveyard, County Wicklow, Ireland
  www.interment.net/data/ireland/wicklow/
                          kilranalagh/kilranalagh.htm

Leitrim
- Leitrim Cemetery, County Wicklow, Ireland
  www.interment.net/data/ireland/wicklow/leitrim

Manor Kilbride
- Manor Kilbride Graveyard, Manor Kilbride, County Wicklow, Ireland
  www.interment.net/data/ireland/wicklow/manor__kilbride

New Kilbride
- New Kilbride Graveyard
  www.rootsweb.com/~irlwic2/grave__yards/
                          new__kilbride__cemetery.htm

Powerscourt
- Powerscourt Demesne (Churchtown)
  www.rootsweb.com/~irlwic2/grave__yards/powerscourt.htm

- Saint Patrick Anglican Churchyard, Powerscourt, Enniskerry, County
  Wicklow, Ireland
  www.interment.net/data/ireland/wicklow/stpatrick

- Wicklow Gravestones Name Index: Powerscourt Demesne (Churchtown)
  www.from-ireland.net/graves/wicklow/powerscourtdem.htm

Rathbran
- Rathbran Cemetery, Rathbran, County Wicklow, Ireland
  www.interment.net/data/ireland/wicklow/rathbran

Roundwood
- Wicklow Gravestones Name Index: Roundwood, St. Laurence O'Toole, R.C.
  www.from-ireland/net/graves/wicklow/roundwoodstlaur.htm

Saint Nicholas
- Saint Nicholas Cemetery, County Wicklow, Ireland
  www.interment.net/data/ireland/wicklow/nicholas/nicholas.htm

Tinahealy
- Saint Kevin's Churchyard Cemetery, County Wicklow, Ireland
  www.interment.net/data/ireland/wicklow/stkevin/kevin.htm
  At Kilavaney, Tinahealy

Tournant
See Dunlavin

Trinity
- Wicklow Gravestones Name Index: Trinity
  www.from-ireland.net/graves/wicklow/trinity.htm

Tyneclash
- Tyneclash Old Cemetery County Wicklow, Ireland
  www.interment.net/data/ireland/wicklow/tyneclash/tyneclash.htm

Wicklow
- Free Genealogy Death Records, Wicklow Church of Ireland, Wicklow Town, County Wicklow, Ireland
  www.ancestorsatrest.com/cemetery_records/
  wicklow_church_of_ireland.shtml

11. Other Sources

Information on a wide range of sources is available on the net. This includes much valuable advice; it also includes many sites providing the actual data. A wide variety of sources have sites devoted to them; these are listed here, prefaced by a listing of sites with database and source collections.

- C.S.I. (Central Signposting Index)
  www.irishgenealogy.ie/csi/csi_main.cfm
  Index to a variety of databases

- DIGdat: Digital Irish Genealogy Data
  www.ajmorris.com/dig/
  Pay per view site, but with some free data, and also many fiche offered for sale

- Family History: computerised family history database
  ireland.iol.ie/irishworld/famhist.htm
  Fee-based list of searchable databases (the databases themselves are not on-line)

- Find My Past
  www.findmypast.com

- Irish Family Research
  www.irishfamilyresearch.co.uk
  Collection of c.70 databases, including Griffith's Valuation, trade directories, educational records, etc. Pay per view site

- Irish Origins
  www.irishorigins.com
  Small collection of databases, including the important Griffith's Valuation

- Irish Records Extraction Database
  www.ancestry.com/search/db.aspx?dbid=3876
  c.100,000 records from 120 different sources - but little indication of what the sources are

- Irish Genealogy Databases
  www.ancestryireland.com/databases.php
  Extensive collection of databases; membership required

- Irish Source Records 1500s-1800s
  www.genealogy.com/275facd.html
  Subscription based index to a wide variety of sources: census, return of owners of land. Griffiths, wills, *etc.*

- A Little Bit of Ireland
  www.celticcousins.net/ireland
  Mainly transcriptions of original sources

- U.K. & Ireland Records
  www.ancestry.com/Landing/product/search/
  uki.aspx?html-uki2&o__xid
  Collection of databases - but no information on what they are and what relates to Ireland

- Casey Bibliography: the mother lode of Irish Genealogy
  www.rootsweb.com/~irish/igsi__published/casey.htm
  Detailed description of a genealogist's collection of notes on 3,000,000 names

- Irish Records Index 1500-1920
  www.ancestry.com/search/db.aspx?4077
  Subscription required. Index to a miscellaneous collection

- Clare County Library: Online Records
  www.clarelibrary.ie/eolas/coclare/genealogy/genealogy.htm
  Collection of databases

- Ulster Ancestry: Free Genealogy Pages
  www.ulsterancestry.com/ua-free-pages.php
  Collection of transcripts and indexes

Admiralty Examinations
- High Court of Admiralty Examinations, 1536-1641: material relating to Ireland
  www.from-ireland.net/history/admirindex/admirintrolinks.htm
  Surname index

Agricultural Census
Antrim
- 1803 Agricultural Census of Antrim
  www.ancestryireland.com/
  database.php?filename=db__censusantrim1803
  Membership required

Assizes
Louth
- Louth Assizes 1793-1799
  www.jbhall.freeservers.com/louth__assizes__1793-99.htm

Tipperary
- Presentments
  www.rootsweb.com/~irltip2/presentments__ndx.htm
  Made at Tipperary Assizes, 1831 & 1837

Business Records
- Business Records Survey
  www.nationalarchives.ie/cgi-bin/
  naigenform02?index=Business+Records+Survey

- Business Records
  www.proni.gov.uk/records/business.htm
  In the Public Record Office of Northern Ireland

- The Harland & Wolff Archive
  www.proni.gov.uk/records/private/harwolf.htm
  Description of business records of the ship builders; including staff records

Catholic Qualification Rolls
Donegal
- State Papers: Catholic Qualification Rolls, 1778-1790. Donegal
  www.ulsterancestry.com/
  ua-free-Donegal__Catholic__Qualification__Rolls.html

- Catholic Qualification Rolls 1778-1790 Donegal
  members.aol.com/lochlan2/donegal1.htm

Fermanagh
- Catholic Qualifation Rolls Index: Fermanagh
  www.from-ireland.net/gene/fermanaghcathqualrolls.htm

Galway
- The Catholic Convert Rolls
  www.from-ireland.net/gene/convertrolls.htm
  Includes list of names from Galway

Monaghan
- Catholic Qualification Rolls: County Monaghan c.1778
  www.ulsterancestry.com/
  ua-free__MonaghanQualificationRolls1778.html
- Catholic Qualification Rolls Index: County Monaghan, c.1778
  ahd.exis.net/monaghan/qual-cath.htm
- Catholic Qualification Rolls Name Index: Monaghan
  www.from-ireland.net/monaghcathqualrolls.htm

Tipperary
- Catholic Inhabitants who swore Oaths of Allegiance to the King in the year 1775
  www.rootsweb.com/~irltip2/oaths.htm

Census
- Actual Censuses
  www.rootsweb.com/~fianna/guide/cen1.html
  Details of availability of the 1901 and 1911 censuses, and of fragments from previous censuses
- Census Links for Ireland
  www.censusfinder.com/ireland.htm
  Gateway; also includes links to sites with trade directories, Griffith's Valuation, baptism registers, *etc.*
- Census Records
  scripts.ireland.com/ancestor/browse/records/census
  Introduction
- Census Returns
  freepages.genealogy.rootsweb.com/~irishancestors/
  Census%20returns.html
  Introduction

- Census Returns
  www.nationalarchives.ie/genealogy/censusrtns.html
  From the National Archives
- Censuses
  www.rootsweb.com/~fianna/guide/census.html/
  Overview of Irish censuses and census substitutes
- Centenary of 1901 Census of Ireland
  www.lalley.com/index.htm?feature.htm
  General discussion
- Ireland: Census Records and Lists
  www.scotlandsclans.com/ircensus.htm
- Irish Census Returns
  freepages.genealogy.rootsweb.com/~irelandlist/census.html
- Online Irish Census Indexes & Records: Ireland Census Records by County: a genealogy guide
  www.genealogybranches.com/irishcensus.html
- Scots and Irish Strays Census Indexes
  rontay.digiweb.com/scot/
  This website has been removed from its server, but an archive copy can be found at **web.archive.org/web/web.php**
- Irish 'strays' in England and Wales Census 1841
  www.irishorigins.com/help/popup-aboutio-census1841.htm
  Subscription required
- Irish 'Strays' in England & Wales Census 1871
  www.irishorigins.com/help/popup-aboutio-census1871.htm
- 1901 Census
  www.proni.gov.uk/records/1901cens.htm

Antrim
- 1851 Antrim Census
  1851.4t.com
- 1851 Co. Antrim Census
  www.rootsweb.com/~irish/igsi__published/cens-sub/ant5100.htm
  Remnants

- County Antrim 1851 Census
  content.ancestry.com/iexec/?htx=BookList&dbid=49109
  Subscription required

- 1911 Census: Co. Antrim
  www.rootsweb.com/~fianna/county/antrim/ant1911.html
  List of Latter Day Saints microfilm

- 1901 Census Extracts, County Antrim, Ireland: Belfast City, Ireland:
  Clifton & Court Wards: 1901 Census Heads of Household Index
  www.from-ireland.net/censusabstracts/ant/1901/belfast2.htm

Armagh
- McConville's Irish Genealogy: the first census of the Fews, 1602
  www.mcconville.org/main/genealogy/census1602.html
  The Fews is a barony in Armagh

Cavan
See also Londonderry
- C.M.C.
  cmcrp.net/Othercty/Cavan1821-1.htm
  Extracts from the 1821 census for Co. Cavan

- Census Records: 1821-1891: Surviving Copies, Fragments and Extracts
  www.sierratel.com/colinf/genuki/CAV/Census/Surviving.htm
  List for Co. Cavan

- 1911 Census: Co. Cavan
  www.rootsweb.com/~fianna/county/cavan/cav1911.html
  List of Latter Day Saints microfilms

Clare
See also Limerick
- 1911 Census, Co. Clare
  www.rootsweb.com/~fianna/county/clare/cla1911.html
  List of Latter Day Saints films

- 1901 Census of Population County Clare
  **www.clarelibrary.ie/eolas/coclare/genealogy/1901census/
                              1901_clare_census.htm**

- 1901 County Clare Census Index
  www.connorsgenealogy.com/clare/#census

Cork
- Names in 1851 Census Records Book, Co. Cork
  myhome.ispdr.net.au/~mgrogan/cork/1851_census.htm

- 1911 Census: Co. Cork
  www.rootsweb.com/~fianna/county/cork/cor1911.html
  List of films held by the Latter Day Saints

Donegal
- Online Census Extracts, Co. Donegal, Ireland
  freepages.genealogy.rootsweb.com/~donegal/census.htm
  For many places, mainly 1901 and 1911

- Names of Protestant Householders in the year 1766 in the Parish of
  Leck, Barony of Raphoe, Co. Donegal, Ireland
  freepages.genealogy.rootsweb.com/~donegal/leck1766.htm

Down
- 1901 Census Extracts, County Down, Ireland: Belfast City, Ireland:
  Pottinger Ward: 1901 Census: Heads of Household Index
  www.from-ireland.net/censusabstracts/down/1901/belfast.htm

Dublin
- Dublin City Census 1851: Heads of Household Index
  www.irishorigins.com/help/popup-aboutio-dub1851.htm
  Subscription required

- Dublin City Census 1901: Rotunda Ward
  www.irishorigins.com/help/popup-aboutio-rotunda.htm
  Subscription required

Galway
See Leitrim

Kerry
- 1659 Census, County Kerry, Ireland
  www.rootsweb.com/~irlker/census16a.html
  Pender census

- 1901 census
  www.rootsweb.com/~irlker/census.html
  Co. Kerry; incomplete

- 1901 Census: County Kerry
  www.rootsweb.com/~irlker/census01cp.html

- 1911 Census: County Kerry
  www.rootsweb.com/~irlker/census11.html

- A Census of the Parishes of Prior and Killemlagh, December 1834
  www.rootsweb.com/~irlker/1834text.html

Leitrim
- Leitrim-Roscommon 1901 Census Home Page
  www.leitrim-roscommon.com/1901census/
  Covers Galway, Leitrim, Mayo, Roscommon, Sligo and Westmeath

Londonderry
- Ireland 1831 and 1841 Census Index
  www.genealogy.com/197facd.html
  Co. Londonderry, 1831, Co. Cavan 1841 only. Subscription required

- 1831 census: Dunboe Parish, Co. Londonderry
  www.rootsweb.com/~nirldy/dunboe/1831cen/1831indx.htm

- Londonderry City, Ireland 1901 Census: Heads of Households Index:
  Partial North West Liberties, Templemore Parish
  www.from-ireland.net/censabstracts/derry/1901/templemore1.htm

Longford
- 1659 Census of Longford
  www.rootsweb.com/~irllog/longcen.htm

- [1901 Census] Transcriptions, Co. Longford
  www.rootsweb.com/~irllog/census/index.htm

- 1901 Census
  www.longfordroots.com/records.html
  Scroll down for Co. Longford database

- 1901 Census Returns for the Parish of Edgeworthstown
  www.mostrim.org/Scrapbook/Words/census1.htm

Mayo See also Leitrim
- Census and Heads of Households, Co. Mayo, Ireland, 1901 and 1911
  freepages.genealogy.rootsweb.com/~deesegenes/cen.html
  Many pages for various parishes

- 1901 census for County Mayo, Ireland: East Mayo
  www.rootsweb.com/~fianna/county/mayo/emay1901.html

- 1901 Census for the Parish of Burrishoole
  www.geocities.com/heartland/park/7461/cens.html

Meath
- People from Meath, Ireland in the 1901 England Census
  www.rootsweb.com/~irlmea2/Census/1901_england_census.html

- Townland Index
  www.angelfire.com/ak2/ashbourne/townlandlist.html
  County Meath townlands

Roscommon
See Leitrim

Sligo See also Leitrim
- WGW Sligo County, Ireland: The 1901 Census Search Page
  www.rootsweb.com/~irlsli/finnsearch.html

Tipperary
- 1821 Census Fragments, County Tipperary
  www.rootsweb.com/~irltip2/census_1821.htm

- 1901 Census Extracts
  www.rootsweb.com/~irltip2/Census/
  For Co. Tipperary

Waterford
- 1821 Census Extracts: Waterford
  www.rootsweb.com/~irlwat2/census/censusndx.htm

Westmeath
See Roscommon

Census, Pre-19th c.
- Seventeenth Century Census Substitutes
  scripts.ireland.com/ancestor/browse/records/census/seven.htm

- Seventeenth Century Census Substitutes
  www.proni.gov.uk/records/17cent.htm

- Census Substitutes 18th and 19th Century
  www.proni.gov.uk/records/census.htm
  Lists various sources giving census-like information

- Eighteenth & Nineteenth Century Census Substitutes
  scripts.ireland.com/ancestor/browse/records/census/eight.htm

- Census Records: 19th Century
  www.proni.gov.uk/census19.htm

Londonderry
- Irish Census Substitutes: A Census of Ireland, circa 1659: Londonderry (Derry) City & Suburbs
  www.from-ireland.net/censussubs/lond/derrycity1659.htm

Church Records
See also Presbyterian Records, and Roman Catholic Records
- Church Records
  www.proni.gov.uk/records/church.htm
  In the Public Record Office of Northern Ireland; includes those of various denominations

- The Church of Ireland: genealogy and family history
  www.ireland.anglican.org/library/libroots.html
  Notes on parish registers and other sources

- Church of Ireland Index
  www.proni.gov.uk/records/private/cofiindx.htm
  Records at the Public Record Office of Northern Ireland

- Church of Ireland Vestry Records
  www.proni.gov.uk/records/vestry.htm
  Brief note

Armagh
- The Armagh Diocesan Registry Archive
  www.proni.gov.uk/records/private/armagh.htm
  General discussion, 13-20th c.

Londonderry
- Bann Valley Church Records: Garvagh Church Visitation Lists
  www.4qd.org/bann/Visits/index.html

Louth
- Tullyallen New Church
  www.rootsweb.com/~fianna/county/louth/loutchu.html
  List of subscribers 1898; over 700 names

Meath
- Protestant Parishioners: Diocese of Meath 1802
  www.from-ireland.net/censussubs/meath1802.htm
  Index to a list of names returned following a bishop's enquiry

Ulster
- Home Towns of Ulster Families 1691-1718
  www.rootsweb.com/~nirdow/parish/hometowns.shtml
  List from the records of Presbyterian presbyteries and synods

- Clogher Diocesan Records: Roman Catholic and Church of Ireland
  www.proni.gov.uk/records/private/clogher.htm

Confirmation Records
- Ginni Swanton's Web Site Confirmation Records, parishes of Enniskeane, Desertserges and Kinneigh, County Cork
  www.ginnisw.com/confirmation%20Records%20Index.htm

Coroners Records
- Coroners Inquests
  www.rootsweb.com/~irltip2/inquests/index.htm
  For 1844-77

Deeds
- Registry of Deeds Service
  www.landregistry.ie
  Click on 'Sitemap' and title. The registry is able to supply memorials of deeds from 1708.

- Registry of Deeds
  scripts.ireland.com/ancestor/browse/records/deeds/

- Registry of Deeds
  www.proni.gov.uk/records/deeds.htm
  For Northern Ireland

Cavan
- Deeds on L.D.S. Film
  www.sierratel.com/colinf/genuki/CAV/Deeds/
  For Co. Cavan, from the Registry of Deeds

Fermanagh
- Fermanagh Deeds (also known as the Brooke deeds)
  www.ulsterancestry.com/ua-BrookeDeeds.html
  18-20th c.

Diaries
- The Harshaw Diaries
  www.proni.gov.uk/records/private/harshaw.htm
  Description of the diaries of James Harshaw of Donaghmore, mid
  19th c. They contain much information on local baptisms,
  marriages and burials

Directories
- Directories
  scripts.ireland.com/ancestor/browse/records/directories
  General introduction

- Directories and Almanacs
  www.dublincity.ie/living_in_the_city/libraries/
  heritage_and_history/dublin_and_irish_collections/directories.asp
  In Dublin City Library

- Pigot's Provincial Directory of Ireland 1824
  www.failteromhat.com/pigot.htm

- Slaters Commercial Directory of Ireland 1846
  www.failteromhat.com/slater.htm

Antrim
- Bassetts County Antrim 1888 Directory
  www.ajmorris.com/dig/toc/__01dant.htm
  Pay per view site

Armagh
- Dave Jassie's County Armagh Research Material Index: Directories
  freepages.genealogy.rootsweb.com/~jassie/armagh/directories
  Collection of trade directory transcripts

- County of Armagh Directories: Pigot's 1824
  www3.ns.sympatico.ca/acauston/genuki/ARM/
  CoArmaghPigot1824.html

- County Armagh: Slaters Directory 1846
  www3.ns.sympatico.ca/acauston/genuki/ARM/
  CoArmagh1846SlaterAC.html

- Bradshaw's 1819 Directory for Armagh City
  www.asaz58.dsl.pipex.com/brad.htm

- Belfast Street Directories
  www.lennonwylie.co.uk/Belfast%20Street%20Directories.htm
  Collection of information from directories, 1843-1907

Carlow See Cork and Waterford

Clare
- Francis Guy's directory of Munster 1886: Ardnacrusha, Co. Clare
  www.celticcousins.net/ireland/ardna.htm

Cork
- Holden's Triennial Directory Cork 1809
  www.failteromhat.com/holdens/holden.htm

- Guys Postal Directory 1914 for County Cork, Ireland
  www.failteromhat.com/guy.htm
  For Cork City, see /guy1914.htm

- Ginni Swanton's Web Site: Cork City Directory 1875
  www.ginnisw.com/Cork%20City%20Directory/Thumb/Thumbs1.htm

Donegal
- 1824 Pigot's Directory: Donegal Towns
  freepages.genealogy.rootsweb.com/~donegal/1824pigots.htm

- 1846 Slater's Directory, Donegal
  freepages.genealogy.rootsweb.com/~donegal/1846slater.htm

- Notes on Donegal towns: Ballybofey, Ballyshannon, & Donegal Town
  (from *Slaters Directory* 1857)
  freepages.genealogy.rootsweb.com/~donegal/1857dir.htm

Dublin
- The Dublin Directories (1636-1900)
  www.microform.co.uk/guides/R97605.pdf
  Guide to a collection published on microfilm

- Dublin Directories on Microfilm
  www.dublincity.ie/Images/DirectoriesMFFeb05__tcm35-11200__pdf
  List

- Pettigrew and Oulton's Dublin Directory 1838
  www.ajmorris.com/dig/toc/__01du38.htm
  Pay per view site

- Shaw's Dublin City Directory 1850
  www.dublin1850.com/dublin1850/index.html

- Porter's Guide and Directory for North County Dublin 1912
  www.dublin1850.com/porter1912/intro.html

Fermanagh
- Ireland, County Fermanagh Directory and Household Almanac 1880
  www.ajmorris.com/dig/toc/__01ferm.htm
  Pay per view site

Kilkenny See Cork and Waterford

Limerick
- Ferrar's Limerick Directory of 1769
  www.celticcousins.net/ireland/lim.htm
  City

- A General Directory of the Kingdom of Ireland 1788: Limerick
  www.celticcousins.net/ireland/lim1788.htm

- Pigot's Directory of Ireland 1824: Limerick
  www.celticcousins.net/ireland/1824limerick.htm

- Limerick City Directory 1788: an extract from the General directory
  of the Kingdom of Ireland, 1788
  www.geocities.com/irishancestralpages/limdir1788main.html

Longford
- Longford Town Directory 1894
  www.rootsweb.com/~irllog/directory.htm

Mayo
- Slater's Directory 1846
  www.geocities.com/Heartland/Park/7461/unindslat.html
  For Burrishoole, Co. Mayo

- Business in Castlebar 1824
  freepages.genealogy.rootsweb.com/~deesegenes/cbb.html
  From a Co. Mayo directory

- Castlebar, Co. Mayo, Ireland Directory 1846 incomplete
  freepages.genealogy.rootsweb.com/~deesegenes/cas.html

- Westport, Co. Mayo, Ireland Directory 1846 incomplete
  freepages.genealogy.rootsweb.com/~deesegenes/west.html

Tipperary See also Cork
- Tipperary Directories
  www.rootsweb.com/~irltip2/directory__ndx.htm
  Includes directories of 1787, 1824, 1856 and 1889

Waterford See also Cork
- Waterford County Directories
  www.rootsweb.com/~irlwat2/directories/index.htm
  Small collection of extracts for 1824

Dog Licences

Carlow
- Bagenalstown Dog Licences 1870
  www.rootsweb.com/~irlcar2/Licences__1.htm

Ejectment Books
- Ejectment Books
  www.hotkey.net.au/~jwilliams4/eject.htm
  Brief introduction

- Surviving Ejectment Books
  www.rootsweb.com/~irlcla/landejectlist.html
  For Co. Clare 1816-1914. General description of a source that lists
  tenants threatened with eviction.

- Owners Whose Land was Stolen
  www.rootsweb.com/~irlros/certificate.htm
  Certificate to move to Connaught or Co. Clare, 1653-7

Electoral Registers & Records

- Freeholders Records
  www.proni.gov.uk?freeholders/__intro.asp
  Discussion of a source listing those entitled to vote.

- Illiterate Voters in Irish Boroughs in 1837
  www.ancestryireland.com/
  database.php?filename=db__illiteratevoters
  Membership required

Antrim

- Freeholders Registered to Vote in the Elections, Co. Antrim, 1776
  www.ancestryireland__com/
  database.php?filename=db__freeholders__antrim__1776
  Membership required

Armagh

- Applications to Register as Voters in the Borough of Armagh
  www.ancestryireland.com/
  database.php?filename=db__votersarmagh1839
  Membership required

Carlow

- County of Carlow: An Alphabetical List of Persons who have Registered
  their Votes ... 1838
  www.rootsweb.com/~irlcar2/1838__voters.htm

- Register of Electors 1920-1921: Absent Voters Lists Parliamentary
  County of Carlow
  www.rootsweb.com/~irlcar2/absent__voters__1.htm

- Irish Free State Army Absent Voters List circa 1926: Constituency of
  Carlow-Kilkenny, County of Carlow
  www.rootsweb.com/~irlcar2/postal__voters.htm

- Carlow Electors Register of 1937
  www.rootsweb.com/~irlcar2/1937.htm
  For Carlow Town

Cavan

- 1826 General Election, Cavan
  www.from-ireland.net/lists/cav/cavan%20election%201826.htm
  List of voters

Clare

- County of Clare, Ireland: Freeholders List for Ibrickane Barony
  www.rootsweb.com/~irlcla/freeholdersofclare.html

Donegal

- Freeholders Registered to Vote in the Elections, Co. Donegal 1767-1771
  www.ancestryireland.com/
  database.php?filename=db__freeholders__donegal__1767__1771
  Membership required

Fermanagh

- Poll of Electors 1788
  www.rootsweb.com/~nirfer/1788__poll.htm

- 1747-1768 Freeholders List of Electors
  www.rootsweb.com/~nirfer/1747-1768freeholders.html
  For Co. Fermanagh

- Freeholders registered to vote in the elections, Co. Fermanagh, 1747-1768
  www.ancestry.com/
  database.php?filename=db__freeholders__fermanagh__1746__1768
  Membership required

- 1926 Register of Electors Killarney Urban W
  www.rootsweb.com/~irlker/elkill1.html

Laois

- Freeholders in the Queen's County from 1 Jan. 1758-1 Dec. 1775
  www.rootsweb.com/~irllex/freeholders.htm

Louth

- 1822 County Louth Freeholders
  www.jbhall.freeserve.com/louth__freeholders.htm
  Also 1824

- County Louth Freeholders 1822
  www.rootsweb.com/~fianna/county/louth/loufree1822.html

- 1824 County Louth Freeholders
  www.rootsweb.com/~fianna/county/louth/loufree1824.html ·

- 1842 County Louth Voters List
  www.jbhall.freeservers.com/1842__county__louth__voters.htm

- 1865 County Louth Voters' List
  www.jbhall.freeservers.com/1865__voters__list.htm

Tipperary
- List of Freeholders of the County of Tipperary in the year 1776
  www.rootsweb.com/irltip2/freeholders.htm

Ulster
- Voters: Poll and Freeholders Records
  www.proni.gov.uk/records/voters.htm
  List of records for Ulster

Waterford
- How Waterford City Voted in 1807
  www.rootsweb.com/~irlwat2/vote__1807.htm

Emigrant Savings Bank
- A Users Guide to the Emigrant Bank Records
  www.nypl.org/research/chss/spe/rbk/faids/emigrant.html
  The Bank was founded by the Irish Emigrant Society for the Irish in
  New York

Emigration *See also* Transportation Records
There are numerous sites devoted to emigration - especially those giving
passenger lists. Sites which deal with just one journey are not listed here
as there are far too many. For general introductions, see:
- Exodus
  www.belfasttelegraph.co.uk/emigration/
  Archived at **web.archive.org/web/web.php**

- Introduction to Passenger List Research
  www.rootsweb.com/~fianna/migrate/pass.html

- Irish Roots
  www.movinghere.org.uk/galleries/roots/irish/irish.htm

- Emigration Records
  www.proni.gov.uk/records/emigrate.htm
  In the Public Record Office of Northern Ireland. Includes pages on
  Canada, the U.S.A., and Australia.

See also:
- Famine and Emigration Links
  freepages.genealogy.rootsweb.com/~irishancestors/Famine.html

Books, CDs, *etc.,* are vital resources, and are listed at:
- Emigration
  scripts.ireland.com/ancestor/browse/emigration/index.htm
  Bibliographical guide

- Ireland Passenger Lists: On the Shelf Books
  irelandgenealogyprojects.rootsweb.com/Old__IGW/passbook.htm
  Look-ups in published books

- Irish Passenger Lists Research Guide: Finding Ship Passenger &
  Immigration Records, Ireland to America: a bibliography of books,
  CD-Roms, Microfilm, & Online Records
  www.genealogybranches.com/irishpassengerlists/index.html

- Passenger Lists and Immigration 1700-1800
  www.rootsweb.com/~fianna/migrate/passearly.html
  Book list for U.S. and North American migration

A number of institutions have useful sites
- Centre for Migration Studies at the Ulster American Folk Park
  www.qub.ac.uk/cms/

- Immigrant Ships Transcribers Guild
  www.immigrantships.net/
  Transcripts of passenger lists from many ships

For records held by the Latter Day Saints, see:
- L.D.S. Records on Irish Migration
  www.rootsweb.com/~fianna/migrate/ldse.html

Other sites with links to passenger lists include:
- Ancestor Search: United States Passenger Lists Genealogy Searches
  www.searchforancestors.com/records/passenger.html
  Includes links to several Irish passenger list databases

- British & Irish Passenger Lists 1890
  www.irishorigins.com/help/popup-aboutio-passenger.htm
  Subscription required

- Dunbrody: Ireland's Historic Emigrant Ship: Emigration Database
  www.dunbrody.com/home.htm
  Click on 'Emigrants Database'. Brief description of an important
  off-line database.

- Emigrants from Ireland
  www.ajmorris.com/dig/fap/rec/index.htm
  Registration needed. Click on title. Transcripts of passenger lists

- Famine: Irish Passenger Record Datafile
  aad.archives.gov/aad/series-description.jsp?s=639

- Irish Abroad
  www.irishabroad.com/yourroots
  Includes a passenger list database. Membership required

- Irish Passenger Lists
  members.tripod.com/~Data__Mate/irish/Irish.htm
  Numerous transcripts

- Irish Passenger Lists
  freespace.virgin.net/alan.tupman/sites/irish.htm
  Transcripts of passenger lists to North America

- Olive Tree Genealogy
  olivetreegenealogy.com/ships/index.shtml
  Passenger list database

- Passenger Lists
  scripts.ireland.com/ancestor/browse/links/passship-a.htm

- Passenger and Immigration Lists Index 1500s-1900s
  www.ancestry.com/search/db.aspx?dbid=7486
  Subscription required

- Passenger Lists arranged by County and Destination
  www.rootsweb.com/~fianna/migrate/shiplists.html
  Comprehensive gateway for Irish lists

- Sites with Genealogical Source Material: Irish Passenger Lists
  freespace.virgin.net/alan.tupman/sites/irish.htm
  Numerous lists, mainly 19th c.

Emigration to Specific Places

Argentina
- Irish Migration Studies in Latin America
  www.irishargentine.org
  Includes list of 'Irish settlers in Argentina', 'Irish-Argentine burial
  records', 'Irish passengers to Argentina (1822-1929)', etc.

- Los Irlandeses in Argentina
  scripts.ireland.com/ancestor/magazine/articles/uhf__argentina1.htm

Australia
- Sources in the National Archives for Research into the Transportation
  of Irish Convicts to Australia (1791-1853): Introduction
  www.nationalarchives.ie/topics/transportation/transp1.html

- Criminals Transported to Australia 1836 to 1853
  www.rootsweb.com/~irlros/Criminal/transported.htm

- Irish Convicts to N.S.W. 1791-1831
  www.pcug.org.au/~ppmay/convicts.htm

- List of Some Ulster-Irish Convicts Transported to New South Wales,
  Australia 1800-1818
  www.ancestryireland.com/online__articles/Convicts2Australia.pdf

Canada
- Immigrants to Canada
  ist.uwaterloo.ca/~marj/genealogy/thevoyage.html
  General introduction to 19th century migration, with many links

- Immigration/Migration Records: Atlantic Provinces, Canada
  www.rootsweb.com/~fianna/oc/canada/can-nb.html

- Moving Here, Staying Here: the Canadian Immigrant Experience
  www.collectionscanada.ca/immigrants/index-e.html

- Grosse-Île in Quebec: the last resting place for over 6,000 Irish souls
  www.moytura.com/grosse-ile.htm
  General discussion; no names
- Grosse-Île and the Irish Memorial: National Historic Site of Canada
  www.pc.gc.ca/lhn-nhs/grosseile/index_e.asp
  General description; no names
- Immigrants at Grosse-Île Online Help
  www.collectionscanada.ca/genealogie/022-504.001-e.html
  The majority were Irish.
- West Ireland Emigration to Canada
  www.teamapproach.ca/irish
- Irish Famine Migration to New Brunswick 1845-1852
  archives.gnb.ca/APPS/PrivRecs/IrishFamine
- Prince Edward Island Data Pages: Irish born in PEI before 1846
  homepages.rootsweb.com/~mvreid/pei/peirish.html
- J. & J. Cooke Ships Passenger Lists
  olivetree genealogy.com/ships/jjcooke.shtml
  Collection of passenger lists, Ireland to Quebec, Louisiana, New Brunswick, or Pennsylvania, mid-19th c.

England
- Hibernia
  freepages.genealogy.rootsweb.com/~hibernia/index.htm
  Irish in the Liverpool area; includes birth, marriage and burial indexes.
- Liverpool Area R.C. Marriage Index
  freepages.genealogy.rootsweb.com/~hibernia/mar/mar.htm
  Includes many Irish migrants.

New Zealand
- N.Z. - Ireland Connection
  www.geocities.com/Heartland/Prairie/7271/

United States See also Canada
- Emigration Lists from Irish Ports to North America: passenger lists from Ireland
  www.ulsterancestry.com/ua-free_Passenger_Lists_1815.html
  c.1815-16

- The Famine Immigrants
  www.lalley.com
  Click on 'Passengers' for various passenger lists to New York and New Castle, Delaware
- IGSI: Passenger Lists
  www.irishgenealogical.org/igsi_published/passlist/58000list.htm
  Lists 5,800 Irish who emigrated to North America pre-famine.
- Irish Immigrants
  www.cimorelli.com/ireland/selectirish.htm
  See also /irishpass.html
  Database of emigrants to the U.S.A.
- Irish Immigrants to North America 1803-1871
  www.genealogy.com/257facd.html
  Subscription based database, presumably from published sources
- The Irish Emigration Database
  www.qub.ac.uk/cms/collection/IED.htm
  Migration to North America, 18-19th c.
- New England Irish Pioneers
  www.ancestry.com/search/rectype/inddbs/1008.htm
  Subscription required. 17th c.
- Irish Immigration to U.S.A. & Canada
  olivetreegenealogy.com/ships/irishtousa.shtml
  Includes various databases, fee-based and free
- Ship Passenger Lists from Ireland to America: miscellaneous ships
  www.ancestry.com/search/db.aspx?dbid=6138
  Subscription required
- Ships from Ireland to Early America, 1623-1850
  content.ancestry.com/iexec/?htx=BookList&dbid=49362
  Subscription required
- Irish Emigrants in North America, Part Four and Part Five
  content.ancestry.com/iexec/?htx=BookList&dbid=49203
  Subscription required
- Irish Emigrants in North America [1670-1830], Part Six
  content.ancestry.com/iexec/?htx=BookList&dbid=49204
  Subscription required

- Irish Emigrants in North America [1775-1825]
  content.ancestry.com/iexec/?htx=BookList&dbid=49202
  Subscription required

- Chicago Irish Families 1875-1925
  www.geocities.com/Heartland/Park/7461/chicago.html

- Chicago Irish Genealogy and History
  www.chicagoirishgenealogy.com

- 19th century Immigrant Roots: Records for Wilmington, Delaware,
  U.S.A. and vicinity: Irish Records for Counties Galway and Mayo
  www.lalley.com
  Includes Griffiths valuation, 1855, for northern Co. Galway; also 1901
  census for Headford and Killursa, Co. Galway

- The Irish in Iowa
  www.celticcousins.net/irishiniowa

- Irish Immigration into Maryland
  oriole.umd.edu/~mddlmddl/791/Communities/html/irisha.html
  Article

- The Irish in Nineteenth Century New York and beyond
  freepages.genealogy.rootsweb.com/~nyirish/research.html

- The Famine Immigrants: lists of Irish Immigrants arriving at the
  Port of New York 1846-1851 ... Ships that sailed from Port of Galway
  to Port of New York
  www.celticcousins.net/ireland/galwayships.htm
  Continued at /galwayships2.htm

- Irish Immigrants: New York Port Arrival Records 1846-1851
  www.ancestry.com/search/db.aspx?dbid=5969
  Subscription required

- Irish Individuals in New York City Almshouse
  allenglishrecords.com/ireland/almshouse-a.shtml
  Continued at /almshouse-ireland.shtml
  List, 19th c.

- New York - Irish Genealogy
  freepages.genealogy.rootsweb.com/~irishancestors/NewYork.html

- Immigration of Irish Quakers to Pennsylvania, 1682-1750
  content.ancestry.com/iexec/?htx=List&dbid=7516
  Database; subscription required

- Rhode Island Irish
  www.fortunecity.com/bally/westmeath/278

- A Brief History of Irish Texans
  hometown.aol.com/IrishWord/Ir-Tex4.htm

- Irish Immigrants to 17th century Virginia
  www.ulsterancestry.com/
            us-free-Irish__Immigrants__17th-cty__Virginia.html

- Irish Immigrants to Virginia
  ftp.rootsweb.com/pub/usgenweb/va/misc/irishva.txt
  List, mid-17th c.

Emigration from Specific Places

- Emigration from Irish Workhouses during the Great Famine, c.1845-52
  www.ancestryireland.com/online__articles/
            PermanentDeadweight.pdf

Antrim

- Emigrants from Cos. Antrim and Londonderry, 1830s
  www.ancestryireland.com/
            database.php?filename-db__osm__emigrants
  Membership required

Carlow See also Wexford

- County Carlow Genealogy: Passenger Lists
  www.rootsweb.com/~irlcar2/ship__passenger.htm

- Cavan Persons in U.S. Records
  www.sierratel.com/colinf/genuki/CAV/USRecords.html

Cavan

- County Cavan - St. Croix; West Indies Bound
  maxpages.com/irishcrucians
  19th c. migration

- Cavan Persons in U.S. Records
  www.sierratel.com/colinf/genuki/CAV/USRecords.html

- Surname Index to Passenger Lists with Cavan Passengers
  www.sierratel.com/colinf/genuki/CAV/Passengers/index.html

Donegal

- Assisted Immigrants from Donegal arriving in Lyttleton, New Zealand, 1855-1874
  freepages.genealogy.rootsweb.com/~donegal/donpass.htm

- Donegal Relief Fund, Australia
  freepages.genealogy.rootsweb.com/~donegal/relief.htm
  Emigrant records of the Donegal Relief Fund 1858-62

- Passenger Lists
  freepages.genealogy.rootsweb.com/~donegal/passengers.htm
  Various lists of passengers from Donegal to North America, Australia, and New Zealand.

Dublin

- A list of Deported Convicts and Vagabonds 1737-1743
  www.ulsterancestry.com/ua-free__Convicts-and-Vagabonds.html
  Convicts transported to North America from Dublin

Galway

- Galway Emigrant Index, 1828-1852
  freepages.genealogy.rootsweb.com/~maddenps/GALWAYEM.htm
  Emigrants to Australia

Kerry

- Lansdowne's Estate in Kenmare Assisted Emigration Plan
  www.rootsweb.com/~irlker/lansdowne.html

- State-Aided Emigration Scheme: Castlemaine
  www.rootsweb.com/~irlker/castlemigr.html

Kilkenny

- Famine Emigration: Castlecomer Area 1847-1853
  www.connorsgenealogy.com/Kilkenny/FamineEmigration.htm
  List of emigrants from Co. Kilkenny

Londonderry *See also* Antrim

- Emigration from Aghadowey Parish, 1834-1835
  www.rootsweb.com/~nirldg/aghadowey/ag__osmem.htm

Louth

- Louth, Ireland, Immigration Records
  www.rootsweb.com/~irllou/Immigration
  Various lists of emigrants

Mayo

- Emigration from Ballycroy, Co. Mayo, Ireland
  freepages.genealogy.rootsweb.com/~deesegenes/ballycroy.htm

Meath

- Meath, Ireland Immigration Records
  www.rootsweb.com/~irlmea2/Immigration/index.htm
  Various lists of emigrants

Roscommon

- Events Leading to the Adoption of State-Aided Emigration
  www.rootsweb.com/~irlros/Admin/old__files/foreced.htm
  Includes lists of emigrants from Ballykilcline, mid-19th c.

Sligo

- Ships Sailing from Sligo
  www.rootsweb.com/~irlsli/shipshesli.html

Tipperary

- Almost Tipperary Emigrant Index
  freepages.genealogy.rootsweb.com/~maddenps/TIPPEM3.htm
  Lists those who paid their passage to Australia, but apparently did not go.

- Tipperary Emigrants and their Relatives
  freepages.genealogy.rootsweb.com/~maddenps
  Includes various databases of emigrants to Australia, 19th c.

- The Story of Ballykilcline
  www.ballykilcline.com
  The story of eviction in 1847, with lists of emigrants to the U.S.A.

Wexford

- I.G.S.I: Emigrants from Wexford and Carlow: 5,500 Emigrants (c.1000 families) to Canada (British North America), 1817 from Wexford and Carlow
  www.rootsweb.com/~irish/igsi__published/misc/wexemig.htm

- Irish Immigrants from County Wexford: New York Port Arrival Records 1846-1851
  users.rootsweb.com/~irlwex2/wexford__immigrants.html

Enclosure Records

- Reports and Returns Relating to Evictions in the Kilrush Union 1849
  www.clarelibrary.ie/eolas/coclare/history/
                          kr__evictions/kr__evictions__enclosures.htm
  Numerous pages listing enclosure evictions

Encumbered Estates

- Encumbered Estates
  www.proni.gov.uk/records/encumb.htm
  Brief note on a source giving tenants' names for many 19th c. estates throughout Ireland

Tipperary

- Encumbered Estates
  www.rootsweb.com/~irltip2/estndx.htm
  In Co. Tipperary

Estate Records

- Estate Records
  www.nationalarchives.ie/genealogy/estate.html
  In the National Archives

- Estate Records
  www.movinghere.org.uk/galleries/roots/irish/
                          irishrecords/estaterecords.htm

- Irish Estate Records
  www.ancestry.com/learn/library/article.aspx?article=1957
  General discussion

- Irish Estate Records
  www.rootsweb.com/~irish/igsi__published/cens-sub/betit.htm
  General discussion

- Irish Estate Records
  www.from-ireland.net/estates/estateindex.htm
  Lists records by county

- Irish Land Records
  globalgenealogy.com/globalgazette/gazkb/gazkb68.htm
  Continued at /gazkb670.htm

- Landed Estates Records
  www.proni.gov.uk/records/landed.htm
  In the Public Record Office of Northern Ireland (but not just for Ulster)

- Church Temporalities
  www.proni.gov.uk/records/private/fin-10.htm
  Discussion of 19th c. estate records of the Church of Ireland

- Private Sources
  www.nationalarchives.ie/genealogy/private.html
  Estate records from private collections in the National Archives

- Records of Private Individuals
  www.proni.gov.uk/records/private.htm
  List of collections of estate and other private papers in the Public Record Office of Northern Ireland (but covering all Ireland)

- 1839 Some Tenants of Lord Roden
  www.jbhall.freeservers.com/1839__roden__tenants.htm

Antrim

- Co. Antrim, Ireland, Estate Records
  www.from-ireland.net/estates/antrim.htm
  List of collections

- 1728 Hertford Estate Rent Rolls
  www.ancestryireland.com/
                          databse.php?filename=db__hertfordtenants
  Co. Antrim estates. Membership required.

Armagh

- Co. Armagh, Ireland: Estate Records
  www.from-ireland.net/estates/armagh.htm

Cavan

- Co. Cavan, Ireland: Estate Records
  www.from-ireland.net/estates/cavan.htm
  List of collections

- Cavan Estate Records
  scripts.ireland.com/ancestor/browse/counties/ulster/cavan6.htm
  List of estate archives

- Principal Landed Proprietors 1802
  www.sierratel.com/colinf/genuki/CAV/Proprietors1802.htm
  List for Co. Cavan

Clare

- Co. Clare, Ireland, estate records
  www.from-ireland.net/estates/clare.htm
  List of collections

- List of Tenants on Colonel O'Callaghan's Estate, Bodyke, 1890's
  **www.clarelibrary.ie/eolas/coclare/history/
  tenants__ocallaghans__es tate.htm**

Cork

- County Cork: Land and Landholders
  myhome.ispdr.net/~mgrogan/cork/a__land.htm
  Gateway to a number of local pages

Donegal

- Civil Survey 1654: County Donegal
  www.ulsterancestry.com/ua-free__DonegalCivilSurvey1654.html

- Tenants on the Abercorn Donegal Estate, Laggan Area, Co. Donegal, Ireland, 1794
  freepages.genealogy.rootsweb.com/~donegal/abercorn.htm

Galway

- Estate Records, County Galway
  **freepages.genealogy.rootsweb.com/~nyirish/
  Estate%20Records%20County%20Galway.htm**
  List of collections in the National Library

- Galway Estate Records
  scripts.ireland.com/ancestor/browse/counties/connacht/galway6.htm
  List of collections

Kerry

- The Kenmare Papers
  www.proni.gov.uk/records/private/Kenmare.htm
  Estate records of the Kenmare family of Killarney, Co. Kerry; the estate covered much of Co. Kerry, and also various places in Co's. Limerick, Cork, Kilkenny, Laois, Carlow, Tipperary and Clare

Londonderry

- Co. Derry, Ireland: Estate Records
  www.from-ireland.net/estates/derry.htm
  List of collections

- The Drapers Company, Co. Londonderry, Estate Archive
  www.proni.gov.uk/records/private/drapers.htm

Louth

- County Louth: Tenants of Lord Roden, circa 1837
  www.rootsweb.com/~fianna/county/louth/rodn1837.html

Mayo

- Mayo Estate Records
  scripts.ireland.com/ancestor/browse/counties/connacht/mayo6.htm
  List of collections

- 1815 Town of Westport Rent Roll
  freepages.genealogy.rootsweb.com/~deesegenes/wes.html

- Marquis of Sligo rent roll: Old Head estate, Mayo, 1802
  freepages.genealogy.rootsweb.com/~deesegenes/rent.html

Roscommon

- Roscommon Estate Records
  **scripts.ireland.com/ancestor/browse/counties/connacht/
  roscomm6.htm**
  List of collections

Tyrone

- Hamilton Rent Books
  www.ulsterancestry.com/ua-free__HamiltonRentBooks.html
  For Strabane, 17-19th c.

Wexford
- Wexford Estate Records
  scripts.ireland.com/ancestor/browse/counties/leinster/wexford6.htm
  List of collections

- Estate Records, County Wexford
  freepages.genealogy.rootsweb.com/≈nyirish/
  Estate%20Records%20County%20Wexford.html
  List of collections in the National Library

Flax Lists
- Irish Flax Growers 1796
  www.failteromhat.com/flax1796.php

- Irish Flax Growers List 1796
  www.ancestry.com/search/db.aspx?dbid=3732
  Database. Subscription required

Armagh
- County Armagh: Flax Grower roster for County Armagh, 1796
  www.rootsweb.com/~nirarm2/records/FlaxGrowers.htm

Cavan
- 1796 Flax Growers List
  freepages.genealogy.rootsweb.com/~adrian/Cavan.htm
  Scroll down to title. Pages for 48 places in Co. Cavan

Clare
- County Clare: Irish Flax Growers 1796
  www.connorsgenealogy.com/clare/clareflax.htm

Donegal
- The 1796 Spinning Wheel Premium Entitlement List
  freepages.genealogy.rootsweb.com/~donegal/flaxlist1.htm
  For Co. Donegal. See also **/flaxlist2.htm**

Down
- Flax Growers of Ireland 1796: County Down
  www.raymondscountydownwebsite.com/html/index2.htm
  Click on 'Flax'

Fermanagh
- Flax Growers List of 1796
  www.rootsweb.com/~nirfer2/Documents/Misc__Records/
  Flax__growers__list__1796.doc
  For Co. Fermanagh

Kerry
- 1796 Flax Seed Premium Entitlement List: County Kerry
  www.rootsweb.com/~irlker/flax1796.html

Limerick
- Flax Growers of Ireland 1796: County Limerick
  www.connorsgenealogy.com/flax/limerick.htm

Londonderry
- Flax Grower List 1796 for County Derry
  www.rootsweb.com/~nirldy2/Old__Derry/Flax__1796.htm

Louth
- 1796 The Flax Growers of County Louth
  www.jbhall.freeservers.com/1796__flax__growers.htm

Monaghan
- Surname Index to the 1796 Flax Seed Premium Entitlement Lists
  ahd.exis.net/monaghan/spinning.htm
  For Co. Monaghan

Sligo
- County of Sligo
  www.rootsweb.com/~irlsli/flaxgrowers.html
  Flaxgrowers list, 1796

Game Licences
- Clare Game Licences, from the *Clare journal*, 1810-1821
  www.celticcousins.net/ireland/cl1810g.htm

- Game Licences: *Freeman's journal*, 27 & 30 September 1809
  members.iinet.net.au/~nickred/lists/Dublin__game__1809.htm
  Issued in Dublin

Grand Jury Records

- Grand Jury Records
  www.proni.gov.uk/records/grandju.htm
  List for Ulster. The Grand Jury played a major role in local government; the records include many lists of names

Griffiths Valuation

- Griffiths Valuation 1847-1864
  www.irishorigins.com/help/popup-aboutio-grif.htm
  Subscription required

- Griffiths Valuation 1848-1864
  www.failteromhat.com/griffiths.php
  Database; national

- Griffiths Valuation: a 19th century Irish census substitute
  familytreemaker.genealogy.com/30__griff.html
  Description of an important source

- How to Use Griffiths Valuation / Public Record Office of Northern Ireland
  www.proni.gov.uk/research/family/griffith.htm

- The Ireland List Griffiths Valuation Page
  freepages.genealogy.rootsweb.com/~irelandlist/anc.html

- Griffith's Valuation of Ireland
  www.lfhhs.org.uk/help/factsh/griffith.htm
  Introduction

- An Explanation of Griffith's Valuation
  genealogy.allinfoabout.com/census/griffiths__valuation.html

- Land Records
  scripts.ireland.com/ancestor/browse/records/land
  Griffith's Valuation, and the Tithe Applotment Books

- The Primary Valuation of Tenements
  freepages.rootsweb.com/~irishancestors/Primary%20Valuation.html

- Valuation Office: Genealogy and Research
  www.valoff.ie/Genealogy.htm
  Brief note on Griffiths Valuation

Antrim

- Ireland Householders Index, County Antrim
  www.ancestry.com/search/db.aspx?dbid=4631
  Index to Griffiths Valuation, and to the tithe applotment books

Carlow

- County Carlow genealogy: Griffiths Valuation of Ireland 1848-1864: Poor Law Union of Carlow
  www.rootsweb.com/~irlcar2/valuations.htm

- Index to Griffiths Evaluation of Ireland, County Carlow: Hacketstown
  www.from-ireland.net/griffiths/carlow/hacketstown.htm

Clare

- Griffiths Valuation 1855: County Clare Surname Index
  www.clarelibrary.ie/eolas/coclare/genealogy/griffiths/griffith.htm

- Index to Griffiths Valuation of Ireland (1855) for County Clare
  www.geocities.com/Heartland/Valley/5946/griffith.htm

- Townland Database and Griffiths Valuation
  www.rootsweb.com/~irlcla/villages.html
  For Co. Clare

Cork

- County Cork: Griffiths Valuation of Ireland, 1848-1864
  myhome.ispdr.net.au/~mgrogan/cork/a__griffith.htm
  Gateway to pages of transcripts and indexes

- Ginni Swanton's Web Site: Griffiths Valuation
  www.ginnisw.com/griffith's%20Valuation%20Details.htm
  Scanned records for various Co. Cork parishes

- Griffiths Valuation: North West Cork, 1851-1853
  www.failteromhat.com/corknw.htm
  For parishes in N.W. Cork

- Griffiths Evaluation
  www.paulturner.ca/Ireland/Cork/Griffiths/Griffiths.htm
  For Ballymoney and Kinneigh, Co. Cork, 1852

Donegal

- 1857 Griffiths Valuation of Co. Donegal
  freepages.genealogy.rootsweb.com/~donegal/griffiths.htm

- Beagh Parish Griffiths Valuation in 1850's: Heads of Households
  www.celticcounsins.net/ireland/griffith.htm

- 1857 Griffith's Valuation: Derrynacarrow East, or Bellanaboy - Stranasaggart - Commeen, Donegal, Ireland
  www.geocities.com/Heartland/Estates/6587/Grif1857.html

- Griffiths Valuation for Inishkeeragh, no.359; Cloghcor; Fallagowan; Gortgarra
  freepages.genealogy.rootsweb.com/~donegaleire/Dongrifinish.html

- Griffiths Valuation for Templecrone Parish 1857
  freepages.genealogy.rootsweb.com/~donegaleire/Dongrifinish2.html
  Continued in /Dongrifinish3.html

Down

- Griffith's Valuation Index: County Down
  www.raymondscountydownwebsite.com/html/index2.htm
  Click on 'Griffiths'

- Griffith Valuation: Lawrencetown 1857
  www.lawrencetown.com/griffith.htm

Kerry

- Griffiths Valuations: County Kerry
  www.rootsweb.com/~irlker/griffith.html

- Family History Library Film Numbers for (Griffiths) Valuations for Kerry County
  www.rootsweb.com/~irlker/griffilm.html

- Griffiths Valuation 1851: Civil Parish of Listowel, Barony of Iraghticonnor, County of Kerry
  www.geocities.com/irishancestralpages/gv_listowell_main.html

Kilkenny

- Griffith's Valuation Index: by last name: County Kilkenny, Ireland (circa 1849-1850)
  www.rootsweb.com/~irlkik/griffiths/index.htm

Leitrim

- Leitrim-Roscommon Griffiths Database
  www.leitrim-roscommon.com/GRIFFITH/

Limerick

- Intro to Griffiths Valuation
  www.geocities.com/jackreidy/grifintr.htm
  For S.W. Co. Limerick

Longford

- 1854 Griffith's Valuation
  www.longfordroots.com/records.html
  Scroll down for Co. Longford database

- Griffiths Valuation [Cancelled Books] (1860+)
  www.rootsweb.com/~irllog/valuations.htm
  Cover Ballymahon Union

Louth

- County Louth. Dundalk Householders 1837
  www.rootsweb.com/~fianna/county/louth/loufree1837.html
  From Valuation Office House Book

Mayo

- Griffiths Valuation for County Mayo
  www.ajmorris.com/dig/toc/mygrif.htm
  Pay per view site

- Griffith Valuation for Co. Mayo
  freepages.genealogy.rootsweb.com/~deesegenes/grif.html
  For a few parishes only

Roscommon See Leitrim

Sligo

- Sligo Griffiths Valuation Records
  www.rootsweb.com/~irlsli/griffithsopen.html

Tipperary

- Griffith's Valuation
  www.rootsweb.com/~irltip/records.htm/#griffiths
  Pages for Tipperary parishes

- County Tipperary Surname Index
  www.connorsgenealogy.com/tipp/SurnameIndex.htm
  Index to Griffiths Valuation and the Tithe Applotment Books

- [House Books: Indexes]
  www.connorsgenealogy.com/tipp/Housebooks-A.htm
  Continued on 3 further pages.
  Index to Tipperary house books, compiled for Griffith's Valuation.

Tyrone
- Griffiths Valuation of Co. Tyrone Index
  freepages.genealogy.rootsweb.com/~tyrone/parishes/griffiths

Waterford
- Griffith's Valuation: Waterford 1848-51
  www.failteromhat.com/waterford.htm

- The Family Names of Rathgormack - Clonea
  www.rathgormack.com/names.htm
  Includes index to Griffith's Valuation

Wicklow *See also* Cork
- County Wicklow, garden of Ireland: Griffiths Valuation April 1854
  www.rootsweb.com/~irlwic/griff.htm
  Incomplete

- Full Name Index to Householders for Griffiths Primary Valuation, County Wicklow, Ireland
  www.ajmorris.com/dig/toc/_01wkgi.htm
  Pay per view site

- Griffiths Primary Valuation of Rateable Property for County Wicklow: Naas Poor Law Union
  www.ajmorris.com/dig/toc/_01wkns.htm
  Pay per view site

- Griffiths Primary Valuation of Rateable Property for County Wicklow: Rathdown Poor Law Union
  www.ajmorris.com/dig/toc/_01wkrd.htm
  Pay per view site

Hearth Tax

Armagh
- Hearth Money Roll, Armagh 1665
  www.failteromhat.com/armaghhearth.php

Donegal
- County Donegal, Ireland
  www.geocities.com/Heartland/Estates/6587/Donegal.html
  Includes various hearth tax lists

- Online Land Records for County Donegal
  freepages.genealogy.rootsweb.com/~donegal/land.htm
  Includes various hearth money rolls

- A list of persons who paid Hearth Tax in 1665 in the parish of Clonleigh, Donegal, Ireland
  freepages.genealogy.rootsweb.com/~donegal/clonleigh.htm

- The Hearth Money Roll for the Parish of Donoughmore, Donegal ... in 1665
  freepages.genealogy.rootsweb.com/~donegal/hdonough.htm
  thor.prohosting.com/~hughw/donoughm.txt

- Hearth Money Roll, 1665 for the parish of Leck, in the Barony of Raphoe, Co. Donegal, Ireland
  thor.prohosting.com/~hughw/leck1665.txt

- Persons who paid Hearth Tax in the parish of Raphoe (including) Convoy, in Co. Donegal, Ireland in the year 1665
  freepages.genealogy.rootsweb.com/~donegal/raphoe.htm
  thor.prohosting.com/~hughw/raphoe.txt

- Persons who paid Hearth Money Tax in the parish of Taughboyne, Barony of Raphoe, Co. Donegal, Ireland, in 1665
  freepages.genealogy.rootsweb.com/taughboy.htm
  thor.prohosting.com/~hughw/taughboy.txt

Monaghan
- Hearth Money Roll: Monaghan 1663-1665
  www.failteromhat.com/monaghanhearth.php

Sligo
- Hearth Money Roll, Sligo 1665
  www.failteromhat.com/sligohearth.php

Tipperary
- 1664 Hearth Money Rolls for the Baronies of Ida and Offa,
  Co. Tipperary
  freepages.genealogy.rootsweb.com/~irish/Tipperary/1664iffa.htm
  www.rootsweb.com/~irltip/Records/HearthRolls.htm

Tyrone
- Hearth Money: Dungannon
  freepages.genealogy.rootsweb.com/~tyrone/info/
  hearth-money-dungannon.html

Land Grants
- Names of the Cromwellian Adventurers for land in Ireland
  www.exis.net/ahd/monaghan/advntrs.htm
  In 1642-6; list of surnames

Cavan
- Plantation of County Cavan
  www.sierratel.com/colinf/genuki/CAV/Plantation.html
  List of land grantees, 1612-13

Donegal
- Lands Grants in the Barony of Raphoe, County Donegal, 1608
  members.aol.com/Manus/dngl1608.html
  This site has been removed from the web, but can still be read at
  web.archive.org

- Captain Nicholas Pynnar's Survey, 1618 A.D. of the land grants given
  in 1608, Barony of Raphoe
  www.finnvalley.ie/history/welshtown/pynnar.htm

Ulster
- The Scottish Undertakers
  www.rootsweb.com/~nirfer/undertakers.htm
  List of Scottish applicants for land grants in Ulster, 1689

Landowners Census
- Landowners in Ireland 1873
  www.ancestryireland.com/
  database.php?filename=db_landowners1873
  Membership required

- Land Owners in Ireland
  www.ajmorris.com/dig/toc/_01irlo.htm
  Pay per view site. Scanned images of the entire 1876 landowners
  census

- Land Owners in Ireland 1876
  www.failteromhat.com/lo1876.htm
  Database of scanned images of the Parliamentary return

Armagh
- Landowners in Co. Armagh circa 1870's
  www.rootsweb.com/~nirarm/landowners.html

Carlow
- County Carlow Landowners 1870s
  www.rootsweb.com/~irlcar2/Landowners_c1870.htm

Cavan
- 1876 Land Owners
  www.sierratel.com/colinf/genuki/CAV/1876Land.html

Clare
- Land Owners in Clare: return of owners of land of one acre and
  upwards in County Clare, 1876
  www.clarelibrary.ie/eolas/coclare/genealogy/
  land_owners_in_clare.htm

Cork
- Property Owners in County Cork circa 1870
  www.cmcrp.net/corkigp/CorkProperty.html

- Land Owners in Ireland 1876: County Cork
  www.ginnisw.com/Cork%20Landowners%201876/
  Thumb/Thumbs1.htm

  Facsimile of the Parliamentary paper

Donegal
- 1876 Landowners Donegal
  www.ulsterancestry.com/1876__Landowners__Co-Donegal.html

- 1876 Landowners, Co. Donegal
  freepages.genealogy.rootsweb.com/~donegal/1876land.htm

Down
- List of County Down Land Deeds in 1876
  www.raymondscountydownwebsite.com/html/index2.htm
  Click on 'Land deeds'. From the Parliamentary returns; nothing to
  do with deeds, despite the title.

Fermanagh
- [Fermanagh Landowners 1876]
  www.rootsweb.com/~nirfer2/Documents/
  Misc__Records/1876__LandownersFermanagh.xls

Galway
- Landowners in Co. Galway, circa 1870s
  www.genealogy.com/users/c/e/l/
  Nancy-R-Celleri/FILE/0005page.html

- Landowners in Co. Galway, circa 1870's
  www.rootsweb.com/~irlgal/landowner__records.html

Kilkenny
- Landowners in 1876, County Kilkenny, Ireland
  www.rootsweb.com/~irlkik/records/1876land.htm

Longford
- Landowners of County Longford in the 1870's
  www.rootsweb.com/~irllog/landown.htm

Roscommon
- Landowners of Roscommon County in 1871
  www.rootsweb.com/~irlros/returnof.htm

Sligo
- Land Owners in Co. Sligo, late 1870's
  www.rootsweb.com/~irlsli/landowners.html

Tipperary
- Property Owners County Tipperary circa 1870
  www.cmcrp.net/Tipperary/Landowner1.html

Tyrone
- [Tyrone Landowner's 1876]
  www.rootsweb.com/~nirtyr3/Land/1876LandownersTyrone.xls

- Landowner's in Co. Tyrone 1876
  freepages.genealogy.rootsweb.com/~tyrone/info/landowners.html

Waterford
- Landowners of Waterford (1876)
  www.rootsweb.com/~irlwat2/landowners.htm

Westmeath
- Landowners in Co. Westmeath, circa 1870's
  www.rootsweb.com/~irlwem/Landowners.html

Wicklow
- Clever Cat Genealogy Data
  users.bigpond.net.au/henrydebi/CCG.html
  Click on 'Gene data' and 'landowners in Wicklow 1876'.

Loyalist Claims
Carlow
- Carlow Claimants: Claims for Losses in 1798
  www.rootsweb.com/~irlcar2/losses__1798__1.htm

Mayo
- Claims of 1798 Loyalists
  www.geocities.com/Heartland/Park/7461/claim1798.html
  In Burrishoole, Co. Mayo

Marriage Licence Bonds
Armagh
See Tyrone

Cavan
- Church of Ireland. Marriage Licence Bonds. Diocese of Kilmore & Ardagh
  freepages.genealogy.rootsweb.com/~adrian/CoIKilm.htm
  For 1697-1844

Clare
- Killaloe, Co. Clare Marriage License Bonds, 1680-1720 and 1760-1762
  www.celticcousins.net/ireland/killaloe.htm

Dublin
- Church of Ireland Marriage Licenses from Diocese of Dublin 1638-1794
  www.rootsweb.com/~irllex/groom.htm

- Dublin Prerogative Marriage Licences (also called marriage bonds)
  www.rootsweb.com/~irllex/dublin_bonds.htm

Fermanagh See Tyrone

Laois
- Church of Ireland Marriage Licences from Diocese of Dublin, 1638-1794
  www.rootsweb.com/~irllex/groom.htm
  For Co.Laois

- Laois Marriage Bonds from the Dioceses of Ferns, Ossory & Leighlin, A-D
  www.rootsweb.com/~irllex/ossory_bonds.htm

Longford
- Church of Ireland Marriage Licences from Diocese of Dublin, 1638-1791
  www.rootsweb.com/~irllog/groom.htm
  For Co. Longford

Meath
- Church of Ireland. Marriage Licence Bonds. Diocese of Meath
  freepages.genealogy.rootsweb.com/~adrian/CoIMeath.htm
  For 1665-1844

Tipperary
- Church of Ireland Marriage Licences from Diocese of Dublin (Tipperary names) 1638-1794
  www.rootsweb.com/~irltip2/groom.htm

- Diocese of Killaloe Marriage Licence Bonds 1680-1762 (Tipperary names)
  www.rootsweb.com/~irltip2/killaloe.htm

- List of Dispensations for marriage for the year 1859. All for the Diocese of Cashel and Emly
  www.rootsweb.com/~irltip2/dispensations.htm
  For Co. Tipperary

- Marriage Licences from the Dioceses of Ossory, Ferns & Leighlin
  www.rootsweb.com/~irltip2/ferns_leighlin_ossory.htm
  For Co. Tipperary

Tyrone
- Church of Ireland Marriage Licence Bonds. Diocese of Clogher
  freepages.genealogy.rootsweb.com/~adrian/CoIClog.htm
  For 1709-1866

- Church of Ireland Marriage Licence Bonds: Diocese of Clogher Extracts
  www.ulsterancestry.com/
         Church_of_Ireland_MLB_Diocese-Clogher.html
  Covers Cos. Tyrone and Fermanagh, and parts of Armagh, Cavan & Monaghan, 18-19th c.

- Church of Ireland Marriage Licence Bonds. Diocese of Clogher Extracts
  www.rootsweb.com/~nirfer/clogher_mar.html
  Covers parts of Tyrone, Fermanagh and Armagh, 1630-1800

Ulster
- Church of Ireland Marriage Licence Bonds: Diocese of Kilmore & Ardagh
  www.ulsterancestry.com/ua-free_MarriageLicenceBonds.html
  Covers parts of Cos. Armagh, Cavan, Leitrim, Monaghan, Sligo, *etc.* 18-19th c.

Westmeath
- Church of Ireland Marriage Licences from Diocese of Dublin, 1680-1764
  www.rootsweb.com/~irlwem2/groom.htm
  For Westmeath

Methodist Records
- The Donegall Square Methodist Church Papers
  www.proni.gov.uk/records/private/method.htm

Municipal Records

Dublin
- Assembly Rolls, Dublin 1766
  www.from-ireland.net/history/dubassrolls1716.htm

Galway
- Galway City Freemen 1794
  www.from-ireland.net/history/galw/cityfreemen.htm

Louth
- County Louth: Dundalk Householders 1837
  www.rootsweb.com/~fianna/county/louth/loufree1837.html
  Rate list

Muster Rolls

Armagh
- Armagh Muster Rolls c.1630
  www.from-ireland.net/censussubs/armaghmuster1630.htm

Cavan
- 1630 Muster Roll, Co. Cavan
  freepages.genealogy.rootsweb.com/~adrian/Must1630.htm

Donegal
- The Muster Roll of the County of Donnagall 1630 A.D., as printed in
  the *Donegal Annual*
  www.ulsterancestry.com/
      ua-free-Muster_Rolls_Donegal_1631.html

Fermanagh
- Muster Rolls of Co. Fermanagh
  www.rootsweb.com/~nirfer2/military_1630.htm

- From the Muster Roll of the County of Fermanagh 1631
  www.ulsterancestry.com/muster-roll_1663.html
  www.rootsweb.com/~nirfer/1631_musterroll.htm

Londonderry
- County Derry 1631 Muster Roll
  www.rootsweb.com/~fianna/county/derry/ldy-1631.html

- County Derry 1631 Muster Roll
  www.rootsweb.com/~nirldg2/Old_Derry/Militia_1631.htm

- Muster Roll on the Ironmongers Estate, Co. Londonderry, Ireland,
  (circa 1630)
  www.rootsweb.com/~nirldy/aghadowey/ironmust.htm

Newspapers
- Making the Most of Newspapers
  www.rootsweb.com/~fianna/guide/newsppr.html

- Newspapers
  scripts.ireland.com/ancestor/browse/records/news/
  Introduction

- A Guide to Newspapers in PRONI
  www.proni.gov.uk/records/newspaper.htm

- Ireland Old News
  www.irelandoldnews.com
  Digitised newspapers, mainly 19th c.

- Nick Reddan's Newspaper Abstracts
  members.webone.com.au/~nickred/newspaper
  Covers 1750-1840

Antrim
- The *Belfast Newsletter* index 1737-1800
  www.ucs.louisiana.edu/bnl

Armagh
- Dave Jassie's County Armagh Research Material Index: Newspapers
  and Notices
  freepages.genealogy.rootsweb.com/~jassie/armagh/Newspapers

Clare
- Newspapers
  home.pacbell.net/nymets11/genuki/CLA/Newspapers.html
  List for Co. Clare

- Index to Biographical Notices in the *Clare Champion* newspaper
  1935-1985
  www.clarelibrary.ie/eolas/coclare/genealogy/
      champions/champion.htm

Galway
- Galway Ireland Old Newspapers
  www.irelandnews.com/Galway/index.html
  Extracts, currently for 1823-4, 1838-40, ad 1909.

Limerick
- Limerick Chronicle Obituaries 1850
  uk.geocities.com/irishancestralpages/lc1850main.html

Tipperary
- Tipperary Libraries: Local Studies: Newspaper Collection
  www.tipperarylibraries.ie/localstudies/newspapers.shtml

- Newspapers
  www.rootsweb.com/~irltip/Newspapers.htm
  List, 19th c., for Co. Tipperary

- Tipperary Newspaper Clippings
  www.rootsweb.com/~irltip2/news.htm

Parliamentary Papers
- Enhanced British Parliamentary Papers on Ireland 1801-1922
  www.eppi.ac.uk
  Database

Petitions
- William Smith O'Bryan Petition 1848/9
  www.irishorigins.com/help/popup-aboutio-obrien.htm
  Petition against a death sentence listing 80,000 names. Subscription required.

- 1916 Petition to split Knocknagoshel from the Diocese of Brosna
  www.rootsweb.com/~irlker/parishpet.html

- [Clare Men in Favour of Union of Britain and Ireland 1799]
  www.celticcousins.net/ireland/1799cl.htm
  List from the *Ennis Chronicle*

Photographs
- Photographic Records
  www.proni.gov.uk/records/photo.htm

Plea Rolls
- The Medieval Irish Plea Rolls: an introduction
  www.nationalarchives.ie/genealogy/crownandpeace.html

Police Records
- County Antrim Outrage (Police) Reports
  www.from-ireland.net/outrages/antrim.htm

Poll Tax
Donegal
- County Donegal Surname on the Census, 1659: Poll Money Ordinances
  www.geocities.com/Heartland/Estates/6587/Doncensus.html

Down
- County Kilkenny Down Surrey, 1659
  www.rootsweb.com/~irlkik2
  Click on 'Down Survey'. Discussion of a poll tax, with list of surnames

Tipperary
- Tipperary Poll Books
  www.rootsweb.com/~irltip2/pollndx.htm
  Poll tax assessment, 1660

Poor Law
- The Workhouse in Ireland
  www.workhouses.org.uk/index.html?Ireland/Ireland.shtml
  Includes page for each union, listing records (click on 'union lists' at bottom of page)

- Workhouses
  www.rootsweb.com/~fianna/guide/PLUwork.html
  List of Irish records

- Poor Law Records
  www.proni.gov.uk/records/poor__law.htm
  In the Public Record Office of Northern Ireland

- Poor From England to Ireland, Dec. 1860-Dec. 1862
  www.rootsweb.com/~ote/ships/irishpoor1860-62.htm

Kerry
- An Gorta Mor: The Great Hunger Archive
  www.thegreathunger.org/html/main/indexa.htm
  Includes digitised images of Guardians' minute books for Killarney, 1845-8, *etc.*

Presbyterian Records *See also* Church Records
- Index to Presbyterian Church Records
  www.proni.gov.uk/records/private/presindx.htm
  Parish records held by the Public Record Office of Northern Ireland

Religious Census
- The 1766 Religious Census of Ireland
  www.ancestry.com/learn/library/article.aspx?article=6702

Cork
- 1766 Census Records Diocese of Cloyne, County Cork
  www.ginnisw.com/1766.htm

Galway
- Leitrim-Roscommon Elphin Census Database (Synge Census, 1749)
  www.leitrim-roscommon.com/elphin/index.shtml
  Covers Galway, Roscommon, Sligo, Ecclesiastical census.

Meath
- Meath, Ireland, Church & Parish Records
  www.rootsweb.com/~irlmea2/Church
  Diocesan census of c.1802

- Protestant Parishioners, Diocese of Meath, 1802
  www.from-ireland.net/Censussubs/meath1802.htm

Roscommon *See also* Galway
- Census of Elphin 1749
  www.irishorigins.com/help/popup-aboutio-elphin.htm
  Diocesan census. Subscription required

Sligo *See* Galway

Tipperary
- Religious Census 1766
  www.rootsweb.com/~irltip2/census1766.htm

Roman Catholic Records
- Local Catholic Church and Family History - Genealogy Ireland
  home.att.net/~Local_Catholic/Catholic-Ireland.htm
  Includes list of counties with their dioceses, much historical information, and many links

School Records and Registers
- Irish National School Records
  www.ancestry.com/learn/library/article.aspx?article=6281

- Research Guide to the Records relating to National Education
  www.nationalarchives.ie/topics/Nat_Schools/natschs.html

- 1824 Survey of Irish Schools
  www.rootsweb.com/~irlker/schoolsur.html
  General discussion of a source for teachers

Clare
- Caheraown National School
  www.rootsweb.com/~irlcla/school.html

- County Clare, Ireland: Kilmaley Parish: Islands Barony: Kinturk School Records 1864-1922
  www.rootsweb.com/~irlcla/clarekinturkschool.html

Donegal
- Register of the old Killybegs Commons School
  freepages.genealogy.rootsweb.com/~donegal/killybegsns.htm

- Raphoe Royal School: students names
  freepages.genealogy.rootsweb.com/~donegaleire/Rapschool.html
  In 1849

Down
- School Information from all parishes in Co. Down, Ireland
  freepages.genealogy.rootsweb.com/~rosdavies/WORDS/Schools.htm
  Database

- The Old School Registers: Lawrencetown Male National School, 1870 to 1898
  www.lawrencetown.com/reg1.htm

- The Old School Registers: Lawrencetown Female National School, 1880 to 1923
  www.lawrencetown.com/reg2.htm

Laois
- Children Attending Mountmellick Quaker School 1786-1794
  www.from-ireland.net/gene/quakersmountmellick.htm

Limerick
- Schools and School Teachers: Murroe and Boher, Co. Limerick, 1852-1964
  www.geocities.com/irishancestralpages/murbohlim.html

Meath
- Ashbourne National School Register of Names from 1870 to 1906
  www.angelfire.com/ak2/ashbourne/reginfs1.html

Tyrone
- Schools Index
  freepages.genealogy.rootsweb.com/~tyrone/schools/
  Miscellaneous sources relating to schools in Co. Tyrone

Ulster
- School Records
  www.proni.gov.uk/records/school.htm
  In Ulster

Solicitors Records
- Solicitors Records
  www.proni.gov.uk/records/solicit.htm
  In the Public Record Office of Northern Ireland

- The O'Rorke, McDonald & Tweed Archive
  www.proni.gov.uk/records/private/d-1242.htm
  Solicitors archives relative to Co. Antrim

- The Martin & Brett Archive
  www.proni.gov.uk/records/private/marbrett.htm
  Description of a solicitor's archive relating to Co. Monaghan

Tithes *See also* Griffith's Valuation
- Tithe Composition and Applotment Books
  freepages.genealogy.rootsweb.com/
  ~irishancestors/Tithe%20books.html
  Introduction

- Tithe Applotment Books and Primary (Griffiths) Valuation
  www.nationalarchives.ie/genealogy/valuation.html
  From the National Archives

- Tithe Applotment Books
  www.movinghere.org.uk/galleries/roots/irish/irishrecords/tithe.htm

- Tithe Applotment Books
  scripts.ireland.com/ancestor/browse/records/land/tiap.htm

- Ireland: a listing of Land Tax or Tithe Defaulters for 1831
  www.alphalink.com.au/~datatree/datree1.htm
  www.ancestordetective.com/ireland/tithe.htm
  Discussion of a useful source

Carlow
- County Carlow Tithe Defaulters for 1831
  www.rootsweb.com/~irlcar2/Tithe__Defaulters.htm

Cork
- County Cork Tithes by Diocese
  myhome.ispdr.net.au/~mgrogan/cork/a__tithes.htm
  Many pages of transcripts of tithe applotment books for particular places

- Tithe Listing for Diocese of Cloyne
  www.cmcrp.net/corkigp/Tithe1.htm
  Covers Co. Cork

- Tithe Defaulter Schedule for Cork 1831
  www.failteromhat.com/tithe1831.htm

Donegal
- Tithe Applotment Books for the Parishes of Killybegs, Upper and Lower
  freepages.genealogy.rootsweb.com/~donegal/killytithe.txt

- Tithe Applotment Book for the Parish of Templecrone, signed 22 Oct. 1828
  freepages.genealogy.rootsweb.com/~donegal/templetithes.txt

Fermanagh
- 1823-1838 Index: Tithe Applotment, Fermanagh
  www.rootsweb.com/~nirfer/
  1825-1835__tithe__applotment__index.htm

Kerry
- Tithe Applotment Survey 1823-37: County Kerry
  www.rootsweb.com/~irlker/tithe.html
  In progress

- Heads of Household of Ballyferriter Catholic Parish, Barony of Corkaguiny, County Kerry, Ireland, 1827-1852
  www.geocities.com/Athens/Ithaca/7974/
  Ballyferriter/compilation.html
  From tithe applotment books 1827-31, a religious census 1834, and Griffiths Valuation 1851-2.

- Tithe Valuation, Brosna Parish, Co. Kerry, Ireland, c.1820
  www.geocities.com/bluegumtrees/griffiths.html

Limerick
- Tithe Records, 1820's: Co. Limerick, Parish of Killeedy
  www.geocities.com/curtingenealogy/titheKilleedy.html

- 1829-1833 Tithe Applotment Books
  www.longfordroots.com/records.html
  Scroll down for Co. Longford database

Sligo
- Sligo County Ireland Tithe 1824
  www.rootsweb.com/~irlsli/tithemcgeeopen.html

- Sligo Tithe Applotment Book
  www.rootsweb.com/~irlsli/titheopeningsligo.html
  Transcripts for a few parishes

Tipperary
- Tithes
  www.rootsweb.com/~irltip/records.htm#tithes
  Names of occupiers for many Tipperary parishes, from tithe applotment books.

- [Tithe Applotment Records, Tipperary, 1828]
  freepages.genealogy.rootsweb.com/~irish/Tipperary/Tithe1828.htm

- Assorted Tithe Applotment & Tithe Defaulters Records, County of Tipperary
  www.rootsweb.com/~irltip2/tabndx.htm

- The Parish of Outeragh, County Tipperary, Ireland
  www.ancestordetective.com/ireland/outeragh.htm
  Based on Tithe Applotment Book, Griffiths Valuation, etc.

Tyrone
- Tithe Applotment Explanation
  freepages.genealogy.rootsweb.com/~tyrone/
  parishes/tithe-applotment/
  List of applotments for Co. Tyrone, including some transcripts

Ulster
- Tithe Applotment Records
  www.proni.gov.uk/records/tithe.htm
  For Ulster

Transportation Records
- Transportation Records 1791-1853
  freepages.genealogy.rootsweb.com/~irishancestors/AusT.html

- Australian Transport Records: National Library of Ireland 1791-1853
  www.ajmorris.com/dig/web/autp.htm
  For subscribers only

- Ireland-Australian Transportation Records (1791-1853)
  www.nationalarchives.ie/genealogy/transportation.html

- Irish Rebels to Australia 1797-1806
  www.pcug.org.au/~ppmay/rebels.htm
  Database

- Irish Convicts to N.S.W. 1791-1806
  www.pcug.org.au/~ppmay/convicts.htm

- Larry Brennan's Page
  www.rootsweb.com/~irlcla/ClareConvictsToAustralia.html
  Co. Clare convicts transported to Australia

- Genseek: Ratcliffe Convicts 1845
  www.standard.net.au/~jwilliams/rat.htm
  List of Irish convicts who arrived in Tasmania in 1845

Donegal
- National Archives of Ireland: Convicts from Donegal to Australia covering the period 1788 to 1868
  freepages.genealogy.rootsweb.com/~donegal/iconoz.txt
  List

- People Involuntarily Transported to America from Donegal 1737 to 1743
  freepages.genealogy.rootsweb.com/~donegal/involtrans.htm

Roscommon
- Criminals Transported to Australia, 1836 to 1853
  www.rootsweb.com/~irlros/Criminal/transported.htm
  From Co. Roscommon

Ulster Covenant
- The Ulster Covenant
  www.proni.gov.uk/ulstercovenant/
  Database of c.500,000 signatures to the 1912 Ulster Covenant

Valuation Records
- Valuation Records
  www.proni.gov.uk/records/valuatn.htm
  Details of various land valuation records in the Public Record Offices of Northern Ireland 19-20th c.

Wills
Introductory Pages
- Probate in Ireland, Part 1: from 1858
  www.ancestry.com/library/view/news/articles/2515.asp

- Probate in Ireland, part 2: Up to 1857
  www.ancestry.com/library/view/news/articles/2923.asp

- Probate Records
  www.nationalarchives.ie/research/probate.html

- Wills
  scripts.ireland.com/ancestor/browse/records/wills
  General introduction

- Wills and Testamentary Records
  www.nationalarchives.ie/genealogy/willsandadmin.html

- Wills and Testamentary Records
  www.nationalarchives.ie/genealogy/testamentary.html
  Introduction from the National Archives

- Wills and Testamentary Records
  www.proni.gov.uk/records/wills.htm
  Wills in the Public Record Office of Northern Ireland

Abstracts and Indexes
- Index to the Prerogative Wills of Ireland 1536-1810
  www.ajmorris.com/dig/toc/__01iwpr.htm
  Pay per view site. From a published source

- Wills Administrations and Deeds, Ireland
  www.from-ireland.net/gene/wills.htm
  Includes various pages of abstracts and indexes

- Wills, Administrations and Deeds, Ireland
  www.from-ireland.net/gene/wills.htm
  Introduction, plus several pages of abstracts and indexes for Co. Antrim, Co. Waterford, Co. Westmeath, Co. Donegal, Diocese of Ardagh, *etc.*

- Irish Will Calendars 1858-1878
  www.ancestryireland.com/database/php?filename=db__wills__1858__1877
  Membership required

- Irish Wills Index 1484-1858
  www.irishorigins.com/help/popup-aboutio-wills.htm
  Index to wills at the National Archives of Ireland. Subscription required.

- Irish Wills Index
  content.ancestry.com/iexec/?htx=BookList&dbid=7287
  Subscription required

- Index of Abstracts, Extracts, and Duplicate Copies of Original Wills, pre-1858
  www.ancestryireland.com/database.php?filename=db__wills__pre__1858
  Membership required

- Index to Printed Irish Will Calendars 1878-1900 (covering every county)
  www.ancestryireland.com/database.php?filename=db__wills
  Membership required

- A little bit of Ireland: Extracted Probates 1630-1655 from Abstracts of Probate Acts in the Prerogative Court of Canterbury
  www.celticcousins.net/ireland/probateabstractscanterbury.htm

Antrim

- Prerogative Will Index 1536-1856 Antrim
  www.ancestryireland.com/database.php?filename=db__wills__antirm__1536__1856
  Membership required

- Prerogative Will Index 1556-1856 Belfast
  www.ancestryireland.com/database.php?filename=db__wills__belfast__1536__1810
  Membership required

Cavan

- County Cavan: Probate
  www.sierratel.com/colinf/genuki/CAV/Probate.html
  Where to look

Down

- Down Administration Bonds pre-1848
  www.ancestryireland.com/database.php?filename=db__down__admin__bonds
  Membership required

- Newry and Mourne Wills, pre-1858
  www.ancestryireland.com/database.php?filename=db__cal__wills__newry
  Membership required

- Dromore, Newry and Mourne Wills, pre-1858
  www.ancestryireland.com/database.php?filename=db__dromore__admin__bonds
  Membership required

Dublin

- Quaker Records Dublin: Abstracts of Wills
  www.failteromhat.com/quaker/quakerindex.htm

Fermanagh

- Prerogative Will Index 1536-1856 Fermanagh
  www.ancestryireland.com/database.php?filename=db__wills__fermanagh__1536__1856
  Membership required

Leitrim

- Prerogative Will Index 1510-1810 Leitrim
  www.ancestryireland.com/database.php?filename=db__wills__leitrim__1536__1810
  Membership required

Londonderry

- Prerogative Will Index 1536-1858 Londonderry
  www.ancestryireland.com/database.php?filename=db__wills__londonderry__1536__1810
  Membership required

Mayo

- Prerogative Will Index 1510-1810 Mayo
  www.ancestryireland.com/database.php?filename=db__wills__mayo__1536__1810
  Membership required

Sligo

- Killala and Achonry Diocese Wills Only: County Sligo, Ireland
  www.rootsweb.com/~irlsli/willssligohome.html
  Index to destroyed wills

Tyrone
- Prerogative Will Index 1535-1858 Tyrone
  **www.ancestryireland.com/
  database.php?filename=db__wills__tyrone__1536__1810**
  Membership required

Waterford
- Waterford Will Extracts
  www.rootsweb.com/~irlwat2/wills1.htm

Indexes by Diocese
- Wills in the Diocese of Ardfert and Aghadoe
  www.ajmorris.com/dig/toc/__01iw3e.htm
  Pay per view site. Index from published source

- Wills in the Diocese of Cashel and Emly
  www.ajmorris.com/dig/toc/__01iw3a.htm
  Pay per view site. Index from a published source

- Wills in the Diocese of Clonfert
  www.ajmorris.com/dig/toc/__01iwcl.htm
  Pay per view site. Index from a published source

- Wills in the Diocese of Cloyne
  www.ajmorris.com/dig/toc/__01iw2b.htm
  Pay per view site. Index from a published source

- Wills in the Diocese of Cork and Ross
  www.ajmorris.com/dig/toc/__01iw2a.htm
  Pay per view site. Index from a published source

- *Indexes to Irish wills, volume II: Cork and Ross, Cloyne,*
  ed. W.P.W. Phillimore
  **www.ginnisw.com/Indexes%20to%20Irish%20Wills/
  Thumb/Thumbs1.htm**
  Facsimile; published Phillimore & Co., 1910

- Wills in the Diocese of Derry
  www.ajmorris.com/dig/toc/__01iw5a.htm
  Pay per view site. Index from a published source

- Wills in the Diocese of Dromore
  www.ajmorris.com/dig/toc/__01iw4a.htm
  Pay per view site. Index from a published source

- Wills and Marriage Licences, Dublin Diocese 1270-1857
  **www.otherdays.com/presentation/archive/
  default.asp?search__a=show&id=1309**

- Wills in the Diocese of Ferns
  www.ajmorris.com/dig/toc/__01iw1c.htm
  Pay per view site. Index from a published source

- Wills in the Diocese of Kildare
  www.ajmorris.com/dig/toc/__01iw1d.htm
  Pay per view site. Index from a published source

- Killala and Achonry Diocese Wills, County Sligo
  www.rootsweb.com/~irlsli/willssligohome.html
  List

- Wills in the Diocese of Killaloe and Kilfernara
  www.ajmorris.com/dig/toc/__01iw3c.htm
  Pay per view site. Index from a published source

- Wills in the Diocese of Leighlin
  www.ajmorris.com/dig/toc/__01iw1b.htm
  Pay per view site. Index from a published source

- Wills in the Diocese of Limerick
  www.ajmorris.com/dig/toc/__01iw3d.htm
  Pay per view site. Index from a published source

- Wills in the Diocese of Ossory
  www.ajmorris.com/dig/toc/__01iw1a.htm
  Pay per view site. Index from a published source

- Wills in the Diocese of Raphoe
  www.ajmorris.com/dig/toc/__01iw5b.htm
  Pay per view site. Wills from a published source

- Index of Wills, Diocese of Raphoe 1684-1858
  freepages.genealogy.rootsweb.com/~donegal/wills.htm

- Donegal Will Index: Diocese of Raphoe, 1684-1858
  www.ulsterancestry.com/ua-free-DonegalWillIndex.html

- Wills in the Diocese of Waterford and Lismore
  www.ajmorris.com/dig/toc/__01iw3b.htm
  Pay per view site. Index from a published source

12. Occupational Records

The occupations of our ancestors generated an immense amount of documentation, much of which is of value to the family historian. An introduction to these sources is provided by:

- Occupational Records
  scripts.ireland.com/ancestor/browse/records/occupation

Apothecaries
- Apothecaries Licensed to Practise 1791-1829
  www.ancestryireland.com/
  database.php?filename=db__apothecareis__licensed
  Membership required

- Qualified Apprentice Apothecaries 1791-1829
  www.ancestryireland.com/
  database.php?filename=db__apothecaries__1791__1829

Clergy
- Fasti of the Presbyterian Church
  www.ancestryireland.com/database.php?filename=db__fasti
  Membership required. Covers 1840-1910

- General Synod of Ulster, 1833: Ministers, Congregations and Closest Port Towns for each Presbytery
  www.from-ireland.net/diocs/gensynod1833.htm

- Presbyterian Synod of Ireland 1833, distinguished by the name Seceders
  www.from-ireland.net/diocs/presbysynod1833.htm
  Lists clergy

- Roman Catholic Parishes in Ireland, 1836
  www.from-ireland.net/gene/romancathdioc1836.html
  List of parishes and priests

- Roman Catholic Parishes 1846
  www.from-ireland.net/diocs/1846/dioceseindex1846.htm
  Lists of parishes and priests

Donegal
- Clergy of Templecrone, Arranmore, Falcarragh, Killult, Raymunterdoney and Tullaghobegley
  freepages.genealogy.rootsweb.com/~donegal/clergy.htm

Kerry
- List of 'Popish Parish Priests' in Kerry, 1704
  www.rootsweb.com/~irlker/popish.html

Coastguards
- Coastguards of Yesteryear
  www.coastguardsofyesteryear.ie

- Officers of the Coast Guard, extracted from a copy of the *Navy List* for 1851
  www.ulsterancestry.com/ShowFreePage.php?id=210

Convicts & Prisoners
Carlow
- County Carlow Genealogy: Convicts
  www.rootsweb.com/~irlcar2
  Various lists of convicts, including some transported to Australia.

Mayo
- 1849 Mayo Convictions
  freepages.genealogy.rootsweb.com/~deesegenes/convict.html
  List of convicts

Tipperary
- Genseek Return of Prisoners found Guilty at Spring Assizes 1845, Nenagh, Co. Tipperary
  www.genseek.net/pris45.htm

- Persons in Co. Tipperary arrested & imprisoned under the Coercion Act of 1881 for Land League Activities
  www.rootsweb.com/~irltip2/arrested__1881.htm

- Nenagh Gaol: Removal of Convicts
  www.hotkey.net.au/~jwilliams4/tgaol.htm
  List, 1845

Wicklow

- Wicklow United Irishmen 1797-1804
  www.pcug.org.au/~ppmay/wicklow.htm
  Database of convicts

Freemen

Dublin

- Huguenot Freemen of Dublin 1660-1729
  www.celticcousins.net/weland/huguenotfreemen.htm

Limerick

- Freemen of Limerick
  www.celticcousins.net/ireland/freemenoflimerick.htm
  For 1746-1836. Continued at
  /freemenoflimerickctoe.htm
  /freemenoflimerickftog.htm
  /freemenoflimerickhtok.htm
  /freemenoflimericklton.htm
  /freemenoflimerickotor.htm
  /freemenoflimericks.htm
  /freemenoflimerickt.htm
  /freemenoflimerickutov.htm

Wexford

- Records of Wexford Freemen found in the Liverpool Record Office
  freepages.genealogy.rootsweb.com/~hibernia/wexfordfreeman.htm

Landowners

- Landowners Map of County Kilkenny, c.1640
  www.rootsweb.com/~irlkik/landomap.htm

Leather Trades

- Kelly's Directory of the Leather Trades 1915
  www.failteromhat.com/kelly1915.php

Medical Practitioners

- The Medical Directory for Ireland 1858
  www.findmypast.com/Directories.jsp
  Pay per view. Click on title.

Merchants

- Merchants and Traders of Belfast 1865
  www.ancestryireland.com/
  database.php?filename=db_merchants_belfast_1865

Militia & Yeomanry

- Militia Attestations Index 1872-1915
  www.irishorigins.com/popup-aboutio-militia.htm
  Subscription required

Cavan

- Cavan Militia
  www.sierratel.com/colinf/genuki/CAV/Military/Militia.html
  Notes on genealogical sources; includes brief list of Chelsea Pensioners

Cork

- Ireland's Royal Garrison Artillery: Hayes Militia Attestations for County Cork
  www.failteromhat.com/hayesrga.htm

Longford

- Longford Militia Muster Oct 1799
  www.rootsweb.com/~irllog/1799_muster.htm
  Subsequent years also available as follows:
1804	/muster_1804.htm
1814	/muster_1814.htm
1824	/muster_1824.htm
1824 & 1832	/muster_1832.htm

Sligo

- The Sligo Regiment of Militia, or 22nd
  www.rootsweb.com/~irlsli2/Military/1802_Sligo_Militia.htm
  See also /Sligo_Militia_1793.htm and /Sligo_Militia_1803.htm

Ulster

- Militia, Yeomanry Lists, and Muster Rolls
  www.proni.gov.uk/records/militia.htm
  List of sources for Ulster

Police

- Royal Irish Constabulary Records
  www.nationalarchives.gov.uk/leaflets/ri2161.htm

- Ireland, The Royal Irish Constabulary 1816-1921
  www.ancestry.com/search/db.aspx?dbid=6807

- Ordering Irish Constabulary Service Records
  www.genfindit.com/ric.htm

- Police History.com
  www.esatclear.ie/~garda/

- Police Service of Northern Ireland: Police Museum
  www.psni.police.uk/index/pg__police__museum.htm
  Includes page on genealogy

Cork

- Royal Irish Constabulary: Cork Appointees 1816-1840
  myhome.ispdr.net.au/~mgrogan/cork/ric__vol1.htm
  Continued at /ric__vol2.htm
  and /ric__vol3.htm

Kerry

- Kerry R.I.C. Record Excerpts for 1848-1852
  www.rootsweb.com/~irlker/ric.html
  Co. Kerry police

Longford

- Royal Irish Constabulary Men from Longford
  www.rootsweb.com/~irllog/ric1.htm
  Covers 1816-46. Continued to 1848 at /ric3.htm

- County of Longford: Award of Pensions on Disbandment of the Royal Irish Constabulary
  www.rootsweb.com/~irllog/police.htm
  In 1919

Tipperary

- Some Royal Irish Constabulary Men from Tipperary
  www.rootsweb.com/~irltip2/ric.htm
  For 1869-70

Post Masters

- Post Offices in Ireland
  www.ancestryireland.com/
  database.php?filename=db__postoffices__1847
  Membership required. Postmasters in 1847.

Publicans

- A List of County Wicklow, Ireland, Publicans in 1910
  www.ancestorsatrest.com/
  ireland__genealogy__data/co__wicklow__publicans__in__1910.shtml

Revenue Commissioners

- Irish Revenue Commissioners 1709
  www.from-ireland.net/lists/
  revenue%20officers%20ireland%201709.htm

Seamen

Cork

- Admiralty Passing Certificates: Cork People (Some)
  www.from-ireland.net/gene/admiraltycerts.htm

Sheriffs

Louth

- County Louth High Sheriffs 1381-1918
  www.jbhall.freeservers.com/1381__1918__high__sherriffs.htm

Soldiers

- Finding and Using Irish Military Records
  www.rootsweb.com/~fianna/guide/military.html

- Service Lists for the Army, Navy & Air Force. Part 1: British Army Lists, 1642- . B. Ireland and Scotland
  www.bl.uk/collections/social/srvlst1b.html
  In the British Library

- Irish Veterans Historical Research Centre Ltd.
  www.irishveteransresearch.com

- Register and Index of Irish Regiments
  www.regiments.org/regiments/rgtirish.htm
  Includes pages for many regiments

- Irish Cavalry Regiments
  myhome.ispdr.net.au/~mgrogan/cork/regiment.htm
  List of regiments with brief notes

- Genealogy Quest, Ireland: Roman Catholic Officers 1693
  www.genealogy-quest.com/collections/rcoffi.html

- The Irish Pensioners of William III's Huguenot Regiments, 1702
  www.celticcousins.net/ireland/huguenotpensioners.htm

- Civil War Rosters: Irish Regiments
  www.geocities.com/Area51/Lair/3680/cw/irish.html
  Names of soldiers in the U.S. Civil War

- 1832 Military Index, Ireland
  www.from-ireland.net/history/allcounties/1832military.htm

Armagh
- Military Records Index
  freepages.genealogy.rootsweb.com/~alisoncauston/
  ArmaghMilitaryRecords.html
  Index of Co. Armagh soldiers found in some National Archives (UK) War Office records.

Carlow
- Military Index
  www.rootsweb.com/~irlcar2/military_index.htm
  Various lists of soldiers from Co. Carlow

Cavan
- Soldiers from Counties Cavan and Monaghan who Died in W.W.I
  orangeroots.tripod.com/soldiers.html

- Cavan Militia
  www.sierratel.com/colinf/genuki/CAV/Military/Militia.html

Clare
- North Clare Soldiers in World War I
  www.clarelibrary.ie/colas/coclare/history/soldiers/
  north_clare_soldiers.htm

Cork
- County Cork Military and Police
  myhome.ispdr.net.au/~mgrogan/cork/a_military.htm
  Links page

- Cork Battalion 1916
  freepages.genealogy.rootsweb.com/~bwickham/corkbatt.htm

Down
- County Down Volunteers
  www.rootsweb.com/~nirdow/volunteers.shtml

Kerry
- WWI Officers from Co. Kerry
  www.rootsweb.com/~irlker/wwlofficer.html

Kildare
- Casualty List: Soldiers from Kildare killed or injured during W.W.I.
  www.esatclear.ie/~curragh/frames_page.htm

Monaghan See Cavan

Munster
- Munster Volunteer Registry 1782
  www.from-ireland.net/history/munstervoluns.htm
  Lists volunteers

Sligo
- [Pensions Records of Sligo Soldiers]
  www.rootsweb.com/~irlsli2/Military/
  1796_Military_Pension_Records.htm

Wexford
- World War I Wexford Casualties
  freepages.genealogy.rootsweb.com/~nyirish/
  Wexford%20Casualties%20WWI.html
  homepage.eircom.net/~taghmon/histsoc/vol3/chapter6/chapter6.htm

Overseas
- Irish Officers in the United States Army, 1865-1898
  www.rootsweb.com/~irlker/officers1865.html

- The Irish in Korea: Irish men and women who gave their lives in the Korean War
  www.illyria.com/irishkor.html

Spirit Grocers
- Spirit Grocers in Ireland
  www.ancestryireland.com/
                    database.php?filename=db__spirit__grocers__1845
  Membership required

Surgeons
- Brief Summary of the Resources at the Royal College of Surgeons Archives
  www.rootsweb.com/~irldubli/RoyalCollege.htm

Teachers

Tipperary
- Some Tipperary Teachers
  www.rootsweb.com/~irltip2/teachers.htm
  Mid-18th c.

Wexford
- Extracted from Education Records held at the National Archive, Dublin, Ireland
  freepages.genealogy.rootsweb.com/~nyirish/
                    WEXFORD%20Teachers%201845-47.html
  List of teachers in Co. Wexford, 1847.

Town Commissioners
- Database of Town Commissioners in Ireland 1828-43
  www.ancestryireland.com/
                    database.php?filename=db__TownCommissioners__1828
  Membership required

Tradesmen

Carlow
- Traders
  www.rootsweb.com/~irlcar2/traders.htm
  Various pages on Carlow tradesmen

13. Miscellaneous Sites

Administrative Areas
- Administrative Regions of the British Isles
  www.genuki.org.uk/big/Regions
  Includes pages on the Republic of Ireland, and Northern Ireland

- Administrative Divisions in Ireland
  www.ancestry.com/library/view/news/articles/2435.asp

- Administrative Divisions of Ireland
  www.rootsweb.com/~fianna/guide/land-div.html

- The Ire Atlas Townland Database
  www.seanruad.com
  Database of townlands, parishes, counties, baronies, etc.

- List of Parishes and Reference Numbers
  www.nationalarchives.ie/cgi-bin/
                    naigenform02?index=OS+Parish+List
  Ordnance Survey list

- Geographical Index Northern Ireland
  proni.nics.gov.uk/geogindx.htm
  Locates townlands, parishes, baronies & Poor Law Unions, *etc.*

- The Townland
  proni.nics.gov.uk/research/local/townland.htm
  Discussion of an important local administrative area

Clare
- Clare Civil Parishes
  www.clarelibrary.ie/colas/coclare/places/parishes.htm
  Gazetteer of civil parishes

Donegal
- Townlands of Donegal, listed by Parish
  www.geocities.com/Heartland/Estates/6587/Dontown.html
  List

- Civil Parishes and Townlands of County Donegal
  freepages.genealogy.rootsweb.com/~bhilchey/DonegalMain.html

Limerick
- Limerick Land Divisions
  home.pacbell.net/nymets11/genuki/LIM/land/landdivisions.htm
  Details of local government areas - townlands, baronies, civil parishes, and poor law unions

- Tir Eoghain/Tyrone
  members.aol.com/lawlerc/tyrone-parishes.html
  List of civil, Roman Catholic, Church of Ireland, and Presbyterian parishes, townships, baronies and unions

Adoption
- Irish Adoption Contact Register
  www.adoptionireland.com

- Searching in Ireland
  www.netreach.net/~steed/search.html
  For Irish-born adoptees

Anglo-Irish
- Anglo-Irish Families in Kilkenny County (1300)
  www.rootsweb.com/~irlkik/kfamily.htm

Biographical Information
- Prominent Persons Index
  www.proni.gov.uk/records/private/ppi.htm
  Information on 5,000 people

Casey Collection
- Casey Collection extracts
  www.rootsweb.com/~irlker/caseyrec.html
  For Co. Kerry

- Kerry Records in the Casey Collection
  www.rootsweb.com/~irlker/casey.html

Chapman Codes
- Chapman Codes for Ireland
  www.genuki.org.uk/big/irl/codes.html

Christian Names
- The History of Irish Christian Names
  www.dochara.com/stuff/irish-names.php

Easter Rising
- Ireland: the Easter Rising 1916
  www.nationalarchives.gov.uk/catalogue/RdLeaflet.asp?sLeafletID=69

Famine
- Sources in the National Archives for Researching the Great Famine
  www.nationalarchives.ie/topics/famine/famine.html

- Famine Relief Commission 1845-1847
  www.nationalarchives.ie/cgi-bin/
  naigenform02?index-Relief+Commission+Papers

Gazetteers
- Ireland Gazetteer and Surname Guide
  www.ancestry.com/search/db.aspx?dbid=3856

- Ireland Topographical Dictionary
  content.ancestry.com/iexec/?htx=BookList&dbid=7262
  Subscription required. Digitised version of LEWIS, S. *A topographical dictionary of Ireland.* 1837. Important for places.

- Subscribers to Samuel Lewis' *Topographical Dictionary*
  www.ancestryireland.com/
  database.php?filename=db__lewissubscribers
  Membership required. 8,483 names

Cork
- Lewis Topographical Dictionary of Ireland: Towns in County Cork
  www.failteromhat.com/lewis.htm

Heraldry
- Coats of Arms from Ireland and around the world
  www.heraldry.ws/index.html

- Coats of Arms in Ireland and around the world
  homepage.tinet.ie/~donnaweb

- Irish Genealogy & Coats of Arms
  www.ireland-information.com/heraldichall/irishcoatsofarms.htm
- Office of the Chief Herald
  www.nli.ie/new_office.htm
- Proto-Heraldry in Early Christian Ireland: the Battle Standards of Gaelic Irich Chieftains
  www2.smumn.edu/facpages/~posthea/uasal/IRHERALD.html
  www.heraldry.ws/info/article01.html

Homicides

Westmeath
- Murders in Ireland 1842-46
  www.ancestryireland.com/
              database.php?filename=db_maureen_irish_murders
  List of persons murdered. Membership required.
- Homicides from 1848-1870 in County Westmeath
  www.rootsweb.com/~irlwem2/wstmurd.html

Huguenots
- French Huguenot Sources
  freepages.genealogy.rootsweb.com/~irishancestors/Hug.html
  Brief introduction
- The Huguenot Society of Great Britain and Ireland
  www.huguenotsociety.org.uk
- Huguenot Surnames
  www.rootsweb.com/~fianna/surname/hug1.html
- 1696-1996. St. Paul's Church, Arlington. The French Church
  ireland.iol.ie/~offaly/stpauls.htm

Jews
- The Jews of Ireland Genealogy Page
  homepage.tinet.ie/~researchers

Journals and Newsletters
- Irish Journals with Genealogical Content
  www.from-ireland.net/jours/journalcontent.htm
  Valuable listing

- Archaeological and Historical Journals
  www.xs4all.nl/~tbreen/journals.html
  Many of the journals mentioned here have genealogical content
- Irish Chronicles Project
  www.ajmorris.com/dig/toc/_011icp.htm
  Email journal, with many transcripts and indexes of original sources. Pay per view site
- All Ireland Sources Newsletter
  www.sag.org.au/new/aisn.htm
  Email newsletter published by the Society of Australian Genealogists
- Irish Roots Magazine Homepage
  www.irishrootsmagazine.com
  Includes contents listing

Cavan
- The Cavan Genealogist
  ireland.iol.ie/~kevins/geneo/index_geneo.html
  Email newsletter

Knights
- Knights Bachelor knighted in Ireland
  www.rootsweb.com/~fianna/surname/knights.html

Local History
- Local and Parish Histories of Ireland
  www.irishgenealogy.com/ireland/parish-histories.htm
- Island Ireland Genealogy & Local History
  islandireland.com/Pages/history/local.html
  Gateway to Irish local history

Look-Ups
- Books We Own: Ireland & Northern Ireland
  www.rootsweb.com/~bwo/ireland.html
- Ireland Lookups
  irelandgenealogyprojects.rootsweb.com/Old_IGW/lookups.html

Carlow
- County Carlow Lookups
  www.rootsweb.com/~irlcar2/lookup.htm

Clare
- County Clare, County Galway, County Limerick Lookup Service
  www.connorsgenealogy.com/lookups.html
  Lookups offered on various databases

Down
- Look-Ups
  www.raymondscountydownwebsite.com/html/lookups.htm
  For Co. Down

- Look-ups
  www.raymondscountydownwebsite.com/html/index2.htm
  Click on 'lookups'. For Co. Down.

Galway See also Clare
- Galway County Look-up Page
  www.rootsweb.com/~irlgal/volunteer.htm

Kerry
- County Kerry Lookups
  www.rootsweb.com/~irlker/lookup.html

Kilkenny
- County Kilkenny Ireland Lookup Service
  www.rootsweb.com/~irlkik/klookup.htm

Limerick See Clare

Louth
- County Louth, Ireland, Lookup Volunteers
  www.rootsweb.com/~irllou/Lookup_Volunteers

Mayo
- Mayo County Lookups
  www.geocities.com/Heartland/Acres/4031/Lookups.html

Meath
- Look Up Volunteers, County Meath
  www.rootsweb.com/~irlmea2/Administrative/lookups.htm

- Lookup Volunteers County Meath
  www.rootsweb.com/~irlmea/lookups.htm

Sligo
- County Sligo: Ireland: Lookups by Volunteers
  www.rootsweb.com/~irlsli/lookup.html

Tipperary
- County Tipperary Lookups
  www.rootsweb.com/~irltip2/lookups.htm

Tyrone
- County Tyrone Northern Ireland Gen Web Lookup Volunteers
  www.rootsweb.com/~nirtyr/co-tyrone-lookup-vols.htm

Waterford
- County Waterford Lookups
  www.rootsweb.com/~irlwat2/lookups.htm

Maps
- Ordnance Survey Maps
  www.proni.gov.uk/records/maps.htm

- Ordnance Survey Ireland
  www.osi.ie

- Ordnance Survey Series List
  www.nationalarchives.ie/cgi-bin/naigenform02?index=OS

- Tom's Big Chest of Old Irish Maps
  homepage.ntlworld.com/tomals/Irish_maps_of_S_Lewis_1839.htm
  Samuel Lewis's county maps, c.1839

- Irish Townland Maps
  www.pasthome.com
  Dating from 1829 to 1843. Subscription required.

Pedigrees

- **Irish Pedigrees**
  content.ancestry.com/iexec/?htx=BookList&dbid=7070
  Subscriptions required. Continued at **49208**

- Irish Pedigrees
  www.ajmorris.com/dig/toc/_0lip00.htm
  Pay per view site. Scanned pages from the book by John O'Hart

- Pedigrees and Genealogical Papers
  www.proni.gov.uk/records/pedigree.htm

- Milesian Genealogies
  www.rootsweb.com/~fianna/history/milesian.html
  Medieval pedigrees

- Ireland Visitation
  content.ancestry.com/iexec/?htx=BookList&dbid=6611
  Subscription required. Heraldic visitation pedigrees.

- Irish Landed Gentry
  content.ancestry.com/iexec/?htx=BookList&dbid=6308
  Suscription required. Pedigrees.

Peerage & Nobility

- Peerages in Ireland during the 17th Century
  www.rootsweb.com/~fianna/surname/dhpeerages.html

- Uasal: a source for Irish Nobility, Heraldry and Genealogy
  www2.smumn.edu/facpages/~poshea/uasal/welcome.html

Plantation

- The Plantation of Ireland and the Scotch-Irish
  www.irishclans.com/articles/plantationmain.html
  Historical account

Rebellion, 1798

- Protestants Massacred in the Diocese of Ferns: Rebellion of 1798
  freepages.genealogy.rootsweb.com/~nyirish/
  Rebellion%20of%201798%202.html

  Continued at /1798final.html

Scots-Irish

- Our Scotch-Irish Heritage
  members.aol.com/ntgen/hrtg/scirish.html

- Scotch-Irish Research
  www.genealogy.com/00000384.html
  Presbyterian Scots in Ulster

- Later Scots-Irish Links 1575-1725
  content.ancestry.com/iexec/?htx=BookList&dbid=4922
  Subscription required. Continued at **dbid=49222**, and,
  for 1725-1825, at **dbid=49220**

Settlers

- Some of the Earliest Settlers in the Laggan Area of Co. Donegal,
  Ireland
  thor.prohosting.com/~hughw/laggan.txt

Surnames

- Ancient Irish Surnames and History
  www.rootsweb.com/~fianna/surname/old.html

- An Atlas of Irish Names
  www.ucc.ie/research/atlas
  Study of the origins and distribution of surnames

- Common Names in Ireland during the 17th century
  www.rootsweb.com/~fianna/surname/dhnames2.html

- Distribution of Surnames in Ireland in 1890
  www.ancestryireland.com/database.php?filename=db_mathesons

- Irish Family Surnames
  www.ulsterancestry.com/irish-names/
  Derivations of common surnames

- Irish Name Locator: 11th to 16th centuries
  www.rootsweb.com/~fianna/surname/nam01.html

- Irish Names: from obscure to modern
  www.namenerds.com/irish/
  Meanings of first names

- Irish Surname Pages
  www.geocities.com/Athens/Parthenon/6108/surnames.htm
  Gateway to sites on specific surnames

- Irish Surnames
  freepages.genealogy.rootsweb.com/~irishancestors/
  Surnames/index.html

- Norman and Cambro-Norman Surnames of Ireland
  www.rootsweb.com/~irlkik/ihm/irename2.htm
  List

- Old Irish-Gaelic Surnames
  www.rootsweb.com/~irlkik/ihm/irenames.htm

- Origin & Meaning of Irish Surnames
  www.dochara.com/stuff/surnames.php

- Researching Irish Surnames
  www.rootsweb.com/~fianna/surname/

- Surnames Common in Ireland during the 16th century
  www.rootsweb.com/~fianna/surname/dhnames1.html

- Surnames Common in Ireland at end of 16th century
  irelandgenealogyprojects.rootsweb.com/Old__IGW/names.html
  Includes page for 17th c.

- Surnames in Ireland
  www.ajmorris.com/dig/toc/__01irsu.htm
  Pay per view site. Scanned pages from the book by
  Sir Robert E. Matheson, based on information from the indexes
  of the General Register Office

- Surnames in Ireland
  content.ancestry.com/iexec/?htx=BookList&dbid=7257
  Subscription required. Based on an official report.

- Surnames: the correct spelling?
  www.from-ireland.net/gene/surnamedisc.htm

- Top 50 Irish Surnames
  www.genealogyforum.rootsweb.com/gfaol/surnames/Irish.htm
  Gateway to sites on specific surnames

- Using Distribution Studies to Identify the Place of Origin of your Irish Ancestors
  www.ajmorris.com/roots/ireland/dist.htm

- www.Irish Surnames.net
  freepages.genealogy.rootsweb.com/~irishancestors/
  Surnames__index.html
  General discussion

Down
- People's Names of Co. Down, Ireland
  freepages.genealogy.rootsweb.com/~rosdavies/
  SURNAMES/Afrontpage.htm
  Surname database

Kilkenny
- Surnames of Co. Kilkenny
  www.rootsweb.com/~irlkik/ksurname.htm

Roscommon
- Roscommon Surnames
  www.rootsweb.com/~irlros/surnames.htm
  General discussion of surnames, with lists of common ones

Ulster
- Surnames/Householders Report
  www.ancestryireland.com/database/php/?filename=db__surnamesSe
  Membership required. Surname distribution in Ulster

United Irishmen
- Wicklow United Irishmen 1797-1804
  www.pcug.org.au/~ppmay/wicklow.htm

14. Professional Services, Booksellers, etc.

A. Professional Genealogists

If you want to employ a professional genealogist, you should first read

- Employing a Professional Researcher: a practical guide
  www.sog.org.uk/leaflets/researcher.html

Many professional genealogists have their own web page. These are not listed here, but many can be found using gateways such as Cyndi's List (see below). The best way to locate a professional is to consult:
- Association of Professional Genealogists in Ireland
  www.apgi.ie

See also:
- Genealogy Researchers Nationwide
  www.nationalarchives.ie/genealogy/researchers.html
  Compiled by the National Archives of Ireland

- Irish Professional Genealogists
  indigo.ie/~gorry/ProGen.html
  List of members of the Association of Professional Genealogists in Ireland, and the Association of Ulster Genealogists and Record Agents

- I.G.S.I. Links: Professional Genealogist and Services Link
  www.rootsweb.com/~irish/links/profess.htm

- What's What in Irish Genealogy: Research Services
  indigo.ie/~gorry/Research.html

- Commercial Researchers
  www.proni.gov.uk/research/searcher.htm
  At the Public Record Office of Northern Ireland

B. Booksellers and Other Suppliers
- Book Publications and Libraries
  www.tiara.ie/books.html
  Many links to publishers, booksellers, periodicals, newspapers, *etc.*

- What's What in Irish Genealogy: Publications
  indigo.ie/~gorry/Public.html
  World-wide listing of publishers, bookshops, magazines, and books

Abeshaus
- Abeshaus
  www.abeshaus.com/new/Genealogy/irish.htm
  Irish books and CD's in an American bookshop

Alan Godfrey
- Old Ordnance Survey Maps for Ireland
  www.alangodfreymaps.co.uk/ireland.htm
  Facsimile publisher's catalogue

Audio-Tapes
- Audio Tapes.com
  www.audiotapes.com/search2.asp?Search=Ireland
  Lists audio-tapes on Irish genealogy available

Books Ulster
- Books Ulster
  www.booksulster.com

Dome Shadow Press
- Dome Shadow Press
  www.domeshadowpress.com
  Small publisher; tithe applotment books of Co. Longford

Eneclann
- Eneclann
  www.eneclann.ie
  CD publishers

Fly Leaf Press
- Fly Leaf Press
  www.flyleaf.ie/
  Publishers of Irish genealogy books

Genfindit
- Genfindit.com Genealogy Records
  www.genfindit.com/
  For online birth, marriage and death certificates, census records, *etc.*

Irish Academic Press
- Irish Academic Press:
  www.iap.ie
  Publishers

Irish Genealogy Books
- Irish Genealogy Books
  www.exploringfamilyorigins.com
  Publisher's site

Irish Roots Cafe
- Irish Roots Cafe
  www.irishroots.com
  Publishers of Irish genealogy

Morgan Publications
- Morgan and Ui Dhubhthaig Publications
  homepages.tesco.net/~morganpublications/morganpu.htm
  Includes many Irish books

Morris, Andrew J.
- Andrew J. Morris's Irish Family History and Genealogy
  www.ajmorris.com/a03/irfamhst.htm
  CD and fiche publisher

- Genealogical Resources from A.J.Morris: Genealogy Publications Catalog
  www.ajmorris.com/roots/catalog/

Quintin Publications
- Quintin Publications: Ireland Catalog
  www.quintinpublications.com/ireland.html

Seanchai Books
- Seanchai Books
  www.seanchaibooks.com
  Specialist in new and used Irish books

Ulster Historical Foundation Bookshop
- Books from the Ulster Historical Foundation Bookshop
  www.ancestryireland.com/ai__books.O.html

Subject Index

Institution Index

Place Index